Student Study G

MICROBIOLOGY:
A HUMAN PERSPECTIVE

Eugene W. Nester
University of Washington

C. Evans Roberts
University of Washington

Martha T. Nester

Prepared by
William D. O'Dell
University of Nebraska-Omaha

WCB **Wm. C. Brown Publishers**

Dubuque, IA Bogota Boston Buenos Aires Caracas Chicago
Guilford, CT London Madrid Mexico City Sydney Toronto

ISBN 0-697-14788-6

Printed in the United States of America by Wm. C. Brown Communications, Inc., 2460 Kerper Boulevard, Dubuque, Iowa, 52001

10 9 8 7 6 5 4 3 2 1

Contents

Preface

You are about to embark on a new adventure, the study of microbiology. Some of you may be anxious about starting because you are not sure what lies ahead. Some may be anxious because they do know what is ahead. What lies ahead are new ideas and a fascinating world of microorganisms. You will discover or rediscover the impact that things too small to be seen without a microscope can have on your daily lives. Hopefully, you will marvel at the fact that something that may not even be alive, and is only a millionth of an inch big, can cause a grown man or woman to cough and sneeze for a week! Hopefully, you will grow excited at the complexity and beauty of your own immune system. Maybe you won't care and you will just want to finish the course. Either way you are starting a new adventure and this can be your guide.

This study guide is not intended to replace your textbook, but instead, to supplement the textbook and to help direct you through the concepts and terminology of microbiology. The Student Study Guide follows the organization of your textbook. Following a short overview of the chapter contents, each chapter begins with a section titled, **KEY CONCEPTS.** This section states in numbered sentences the major concepts from the chapter in a direct, applied, and usually nontechnical fashion. As you begin to study a chapter, and usually before the material is presented in class, you should read these concepts because they introduce you to the chapter.

The next section is the **SUMMARY**. This is an outline of the topics in the chapter and should help you in your reading and understanding of how ideas and concepts fit together and are related. Before you begin to read the chapter, it would be a good idea to browse through the summary to help organize your own thoughts. The summary is also helpful in taking reading notes as you proceed with your reading assignments. Use it to fill in details from your reading and from your class. It is usually very helpful if you have read the key concepts and summary before going to a lecture class. In addition, you will probably find it helpful to page through the textbook and identify the terms in bold lettering before you go to lecture. When you hear the terms in class they will not sound so foreign if you have already seen them once or twice.

The new terminology associated with microbiology is often one of the most difficult aspects of learning this or any new subject. To help with this, the section **TERMS AND DEFINITIONS,** which appears in most chapters, provides you with definitions that are directly or closely paraphrased from your textbook. Practice with these terms should help you master their meanings. When you have finished your reading, you can test your knowledge in the **SELF-TEST OF READING MATERIAL.** This section offers you the opportunity to through multiple choice or matching questions to see if you have comprehended the reading material. The questions typically reflect the major concepts and sections of the chapter. Answers are provided so you may check immediately to see how you did.

The final section, **REVIEW QUESTIONS,** includes written questions that ask you to recall some text material or to think about something and synthesize a new answer. You can derive the most benefit from this section if you write out the answers because you will use the terms and arrange ideas into a specific answer. Hopefully, you will even find some of the questions fun and interesting.

Regardless of your reasons or approach to studying microbiology, enjoy yourself.

1 MICROBIOLOGY IN THE BIOLOGICAL WORLD

This chapter provides an introduction to microbiology with a discussion of significant milestones that have been important in the development of microbiology. It also defines new directions for microbiologists of the future. The concepts of cell theory and cellular types are introduced along with a description of the origin of eukaryotic cells. The chapter concludes with a description of the various members of the microbial world and how we name them.

KEY CONCEPTS

1. Microorganisms have determined the course of history because of the diseases they cause.
2. New infectious diseases appear as lifestyles change, people travel to exotic places, and techniques for growing and identifying organisms and viruses improve.
3. Cells are the basic units of life, and all cells must carry out the same critical functions in order to survive.
4. Two major types of cells exist: the prokaryotes, which do not contain a "true" nucleus or other membrane-bound internal structures, and the eukaryotes, which do contain a true nucleus.
5. The microbial world consists of prokaryotes and eukaryotes, as well as non-living agents, the viruses and viroids.
6. All bacteria are prokaryotes, and can be further divided into two large groups based on their chemical compositions.

SUMMARY

I. Introduction
  A. Microorganisms are, in large part, responsible for determining the course of human history.
  B. The use of modern sanitation facilities, vaccinations, as well as antibiotics has dramatically reduced the incidence of infectious disease.

II. Microorganisms Discovered
  A. Anton van Leeuwenhoek discovered microorganisms over 300 years ago by viewing water samples through lenses that magnified three hundredfold.
  B. The theory of spontaneous generation was revived with the discovery of the microbial world.
    1. Differing results from different investigators lead to the controversy of whether living organisms could arise from dead organic matter. This controversy was not resolved until the 1860s.
    2. Pasteur demonstrated that the air is filled with microorganisms and showed that swan-necked flasks containing sterile infusions could remain sterile indefinitely.
    3. Tyndall, and independently, Cohn discovered that heat-resistant forms of bacteria, or endospores, were present in certain infusions.

III. Medical Microbiology—Past Triumphs
  A. Between 1875 and 1918, most disease-causing bacteria were identified.

IV. Medical Microbiology—Future Challenges
  A. "New" diseases are appearing. These included Legionnaires' disease, toxic shock syndrome, Lyme disease, AIDS, and hantavirus disease.
  B. Many diseases that were on the wane are now increasing in frequency. These include mumps, whooping cough, diphtheria, and most recently, tuberculosis.
  C. Organisms are becoming increasingly resistant to antibiotics.

V. Beneficial Applications of Microbiology—Past and Present
  A. Human life could not exist without the activity of microorganisms.
  B. Microorganisms have been used for centuries for food production.

VI. Biotechnology—New Applications for Microorganisms
  A. Microorganisms are now being developed to produce vaccines, clean up the environment, and carry out many other processes designed to make life more comfortable.

VII. Cell Theory
  A. Schleiden and Schwann in the mid-1800s proposed the cell theory—that cells are the basic units of life.

VIII. Similarity in Function and Composition of All Cells
  A. All cells growing independently of other cells, such as bacteria, have one basic function—to reproduce. To do this, they must generate energy and synthesize the components of living matter.
  B. All cells are composed of the same macromolecules, such as nucleic acids (DNA and RNA) and proteins, which, in turn, are composed of the same subunits.

IX. Basic Cell Types
  A. There are two cell types: prokaryotic and eukaryotic. Prokaryotic cells are simple, without membrane-bound internal structures. Eukaryotic cells are larger, more complex, and have several internal membrane-bound structures. All bacteria are prokaryotic; algae, fungi, and protozoa are eukaryotic.
  B. A cell type has been found that appears to be intermediate between prokaryotes and eukaryotes; it has a true nucleus but no mitochondria.
  C. Bacteria can be divided into two major groups, the eubacteria and the archaebacteria.
      1. Both groups are similar microscopically, but differ in the chemical composition of several structures.
      2. The two groups are not closely related to each other or to the eukaryotes.
  D. Eubacteria include most bacteria familiar to microbiologists.
      1. This group is very diverse.
      2. The "typical" bacteria, which include both eubacteria and archaebacteria, are the most common and although they are also heterogeneous, they do share some obvious properties.
  E. Archaebacteria often grow under extreme conditions of temperature and salinity.

X. Members of the Microbial World
  A. The members include all unicellular organisms, which includes all prokaryotes.
  B. Algae, fungi, and protozoa are the eukaryotic members of the microbial world.
  C. Viruses, viroids, and prions are non-living members of the microbial world.

XI. Nomenclature of Organisms
  A. All organisms are named according to the binomial system of genus and species.
  B. Names and descriptions of most bacteria are published in *Bergey's Manual of Systematic Bacteriology*.

TERMS AND DEFINITIONS

1. _____ is a technique of microscopy in which faint objects appear brightly lit against a dark background.

2. The hypothesis that a cell with a nucleus engulfed other prokaryotic cells which eventually evolved into mitochondria and chloroplasts is known as the _____ theory.

3. Organisms that can be seen only with the aid of a microscope are called _____ .

4. _____ is a process by which living microorganisms are used to help clean up the environment.

5. _____ are heat-resistant, non-dividing forms of bacteria.

6. A unique chemical compound found only in the cell wall of bacteria is called _____ .

7. _____ consist of a piece of genetic material surrounded by a protective protein coat.

8. The system developed by Linnaeus for naming organisms is known as the _____ system of nomenclature.

9. _____ is a specialized group of cells that performs a specific function.

10. The _____ states that all organisms are composed of cells and that cells are the fundamental units of life.

11. Cells that do not have a membrane surrounding their genetic material are known as _____ cells.

12. A specialized group of tissues that performs a specific function is called an _____.

13. Cells that have a membrane surrounding their genetic material are known as _____ cells.

SELF-TEST OF READING MATERIAL

1. Leeuwenhoek's discoveries were significant because
   a. he was the first person to use a microscope.
   b. he carefully recorded and reported his results.
   c. of his finely ground lenses.
   d. he was a renowned scientist of his day.
   e. he limited his observations.

2. Infectious diseases have essentially been eliminated by antibiotics and vaccination and are no longer a public health problem.
   a. True
   b. False

3. Diseases once thought to be controlled that are reappearing in developed countries include
   1. measles
   2. whooping cough
   3. AIDS
   4. tuberculosis
   5. mumps
   a. 1,2,3,4
   b. 2,3,4,5
   c. 3
   d. 2,4,5
   e. 1,3,4,5

4. The number of disease-producing microorganisms is _____ of the total number of microorganisms.
   a. a very large proportion
   b. about half
   c. a very small proportion

5. The discovery of the microbial world by Leeuwenhoek created a controversy that lasted almost 300 years. This controversy centered on
   a. the causes of disease.
   b. spontaneous generation.
   c. flies and maggots.
   d. the church and the scientist.
   e. the origin of life.

6. Pasteur's experiments demonstrated that microorganisms in the _____ were indistinguishable from those that grew in contaminated flasks.
   a. corks
   b. broth
   c. air
   d. water
   e. soil

7. Tyndall, and independently Cohn, discovered a heat-resistant form of bacteria. This bacterial stage became known as a(n)
   a. exospore.
   b. vegetative cell.
   c. prokaryotic cell.
   d. cell wall.
   e. endospore.

3

8. The cell theory states that
   a. cells come from other cells.
   b. cells are the fundamental units of life.
   c. all organisms are composed of cells.
   d. Only b. and c. are correct
   e. a., b., and c. are correct.

9. The original distinction between the two types of cells, prokaryotic and eukaryotic, was made on the basis of the
   a. structure of the cell wall.
   b. absence or presence of mitochondria.
   c. absence or presence of a nuclear membrane.
   d. absence or presence of ribosomes.
   e. structure of the cell membrane.

10. Bacteria, with the exception of archaebacteria, are prokaryotic cells.
    a. True
    b. False

11. While the eubacteria, the "typical" bacteria, are a heterogeneous group, they do share some features in common. Which of the following features are shared by the eubacteria?
    1. single-celled prokaryotes
    2. rigid cell walls with peptidoglycan
    3. single-celled eukaryotes
    4. multiply by binary fission; one cell divides into two
    5. rigid cell walls with cellulose
    a. 1,2,4
    b. 2,3,4
    c. 3,4,5
    d. 1,2
    e. 3,5

12. The hypothesis that organelles such as mitochondria and chloroplasts in eukaryotic cells evolved from prokaryotic organisms which were engulfed by primitive nucleated cells is known as the
    a. cell theory.
    b. endospore theory.
    c. endosymbiotic theory.
    d. bioremediation theory.
    e. Schleiden and Schwann theory.

13. Which of the following would probably not be included in the microbial kingdom?
    a. all single-celled organisms
    b. multicellular organisms with a cellular level of organization
    c. organisms with tissues and organs
    d. all single-celled eukaryotes
    e. all prokaryotes

14. We cannot describe viruses as prokaryotes or eukaryotes because viruses
    a. are not living.
    b. are agents and not organisms.
    c. were discovered after prokaryotes and eukaryotes.
    d. are not cellular.
    e. do not contain any genetic information.

15. Viruses are too small to contain all of the machinery and molecules necessary for life.
    a. True
    b. False

16. Which of the following is a correct way to represent the scientific name for a specific bacterium?
    a. *Bacillus cereus*
    b. *Bacillus Cereus*
    c. bacillus cereus
    d. Bacillus cereus
    e. bacillus Cereus

REVIEW QUESTIONS

1. What is the argument for including multicellular organisms such as algae and mushrooms in the microbial kingdom?

2. What problems contributed to the confusion of the early investigations into spontaneous generation?

3. Describe a few ways in which biotechnology might improve our lives now and in the future.

ANSWERS:

Terms and Definitions
1. darkfield illumination 2. endosymbiosis 3. microorganisms 4. bioremediation 5. endospores
6. peptidoglycan 7. viruses 8. binomial 9. tissue 10. cell theory 11. prokaryotic 12. organ 13. eukaryotic

Self-Test of Reading Material
1. b 2. b 3. d 4. c 5. b 6. c 7. e 8. e 9. c 10. b 11. a 12. c 13. c 14. d 15. a 16. a

NOTES

2 BIOCHEMISTRY OF THE MOLECULES OF LIFE

To understand how microorganisms live and die, produce disease, and do all of the other amazing things they do, requires some working knowledge of chemistry. This chapter presents the fundamental concepts of the chemistry of living organisms. It starts with the atom, the simplest level of organization, and moves to higher levels, finishing with the macromolecules. The structure and function of proteins, polysaccharides, nucleic acids, and lipids are described.

KEY CONCEPTS

1. Four elements, carbon, oxygen, hydrogen and nitrogen make up over 98% of all living matter. Two other elements, phosphorus and sulfur, are also very important.
2. The bonds that hold atoms together result from electrons interacting with each other. Bonds vary in strength and in the arrangement of electrons, which gives molecules characteristic properties.
3. Weak bonds are important in biological systems, since they often determine the most important properties of the molecules and are responsible for their proper functioning.
4. All life is based on the bonding properties of water which comprises over 90% of the cell's weight.
5. Macromolecules consist of many repeating subunits, each subunit consisting of a small, simple molecule. The subunits are first synthesized, then bonded together to form the macromolecule.

SUMMARY

I. Elements and Atoms
   A. An element is a pure substance that consists of a single type of atom. Atoms are the basic units of all matter. They consist of three major components: electrons, protons, and neutrons.

II. Formation of Molecules: Chemical Bonds
   A. Chemical bonds are of two types: strong and weak. The stronger the bond, the more energy is required to break it.
   B. Strong bonds are usually covalent bonds formed when atoms share electrons to fill their outer shell and thereby achieve maximum stability.
      1. Covalent bonds vary in their distribution of shared electrons, which results in the molecule having a positive and negative charge at different sites.
   C. Ionic bonds are formed by the loss and gain of electrons between atoms. In aqueous solutions, they are weak.
   D. Hydrogen bonds are weak but biologically very important. They hold the two strands of DNA together and are important in determining the shape of proteins.
      1. They result from the attraction of positively charged H atoms to negatively charged N or O atoms.

III. Important Molecules of Life
   A. Small molecules in the cell are both organic and inorganic.
      1. The inorganic molecules include many that are required for enzyme function.
      2. Organic molecules are mainly compounds that are being metabolized or molecules that are the subunits of macromolecules.
   B. All very large molecules in the cell (macromolecules) consist of repeating subunits called monomers.
      1. There are three important macromolecules. Proteins are chains of amino acids that form a polypeptide. Polysaccharides are chains of monosaccharides that form branching structures. Nucleic acids are DNA and RNA which are chains of nucleotides.
   C. Proteins are polymers of amino acids.
      1. Amino acid. Consists of a molecule with a carboxyl group and an amino group bonded to the same carbon atom. The carbon atom is bonded to a side chain. Twenty different amino acids, each differing in their side chains, are present in proteins.

2. Peptide bond synthesis. A covalent bond is formed between the amino group of one amino acid and the carboxyl group of the adjacent amino acid with the removal of HOH (dehydration synthesis).
3. Levels of protein structure. Three features characterize a protein: (1) its primary structure, (2) its shape, whether globular or long fibers, and (3) whether or not the protein consists of one or several polypeptide chains. A variety of weak bonds are involved in maintaining the three-dimensional shape of proteins.
4. Substitute proteins contain covalently bonded molecules other than amino acids. These include glycoproteins (sugars) and lipoproteins (lipids).

D. Polysaccharides are polymers of monosaccharide (carbohydrate) subunits. Carbohydrates (sugars) contain a large number of alcohol groups (-OH) in which the C atom is also bonded to an H atom to form H-C-OH.
1. Monosaccharides are the subunits of polysaccharides. The most common are pentoses (5C) and hexoses (6C).
2. Disaccharides are two monosaccharides joined together with a loss of water (dehydration synthesis).
3. Different polysaccharides vary in size, their degree of branching, bonding of monosaccharides to one another, and the monosaccharides involved.

E. Nucleic acids, which include deoxyribonucleic acid (DNA) and ribonucleic acid (RNA),are polymers of nucleotide subunits and are unbranched.
1. DNA. The nucleotides are composed of three units: a nitrogen base [purine (adenine or guanine) or pyrimidine (thymine or cytosine)], covalently bonded to deoxyribose, which, in turn, is bonded to a phosphate molecule. A phosphate bonded to the sugar molecule joins the nucleotides together. DNA occurs in the cell as a double-stranded helix in which the two strands are held together by hydrogen bonding between adenine and thymine and between guanine and cytosine.
2. Ribonucleic acid (RNA). Nucleotides are the same as in DNA except that ribose replaces deoxyribose, and uracil replaces thymine. RNA is shorter in length and does not occur as a double helix. Three different types of RNA exist in the cell.

F. Lipids are biologically important but are too small and heterogeneous to be considered macromolecules.
1. All lipids have one property in common—they are insoluble in water, but soluble in organic solvents. This difference in solubility is due to their nonpolar, hydrophobic nature.
2. They are not composed of similar subunits but rather of a variety of substances that differ in chemical structure.
3. Simple lipids, which contain only C, H, and O, include fats and steroids. Fats are composed of glycerol covalently bonded to fatty acids. Steroids have a four-membered ring structure.
4. Compound lipids contain fatty acids and glycerol and, in addition, often elements other than C, H, and O. They include phospholipids, lipoproteins, and lipopolysaccharides. They all play important roles in the cell envelope of bacteria.
5. Phospholipids consist of two parts, each with different properties. One end is polar and therefore is soluble in water. The other end, containing only C and H, is nonpolar and therefore insoluble in water, but soluble in organic solvents.

TERMS AND DEFINITIONS

1. A weak bond formed as a result of a hydrogen atom covalently bonding to an oxygen or nitrogen atom

   is called a _____ .

2. A strong bond made by sharing electrons between atoms is a _____ .

3. _____ are lipids that are liquids at room temperature.

4. Polymers are made from their monomer units by the process of _____ .

5. _____ are negatively charged particles that participate in the bonding of atoms.

6. Membrane molecules that have both hydrophobic and hydrophilic parts are known as _____ .

7. Sucrose is an example of a _____ .

8. Atomic particles found in the nucleus of an atom that do not have an electrical charge

   are called _____ .

9. _____ are the monomers or building blocks of nucleic acids.

10. Proteins, polysaccharides, and nucleic acids are examples of very large molecules called _____ .

11. The combination of fatty acids and glycerol which are solids at room temperature

   are known as _____ .

12. _____ bonds involve the complete transfer of electrons from one atom to another.

13. Large molecules formed by joining together the same small molecules or monomers,

   are called _____ .

14. Protein molecules are held in their three-dimensional shape by _____ bonds and

   _____ bridges.

SELF-TEST OF READING MATERIAL

1. The sodium ion, Na^+, has a single positive charge because it has
   a. more neutrons in its nucleus than electrons in orbit.
   b. more electrons in its nucleus than protons in orbit.
   c. six electrons.
   d. more protons in its nucleus than electrons in orbit.
   e. more electrons in its nucleus than neutrons in orbit.

2. Atoms are electrically neutral. Which of the following has an electrical charge?
   1. protons   4. neutrons
   2. electrons   5. atoms
   3. ions
      a. 1,3,5   d. 3
      b. 3,4,5   e. 1,2,3,4,5
      c. 1,2,3

3. The number of protons in the nucleus of an atom is its
   a. atomic number.   d. molecular weight.
   b. number of electron orbitals.   e. valence.
   c. atomic weight.

4. Weak bonds that are responsible for holding the strands of DNA together are
   a. ionic bonds.   d. nitrogen bonds.
   b. hydrogen bonds.   e. water bonds.
   c. disulfide bonds.

5. Biological molecules made by covalently bonding amino acids are called
   a. proteins.   d. disaccharides.
   b. lipids.   e. polysaccharides.
   c. nucleic acids.

9

6. All macromolecules share the common feature of being synthesized by joining subunits or monomers together. This joining process is known as
   a. hydrolysis.
   b. dehydration synthesis.
   c. hydrogen bonding
   d. hydration synthesis.
   e. dehydrolysis.

7. The number and sequence of amino acids determines the
   a. primary structure of a polysaccharide.
   b. secondary structure of a protein.
   c. the secondary structure of a polysaccharide.
   d. the primary structure of a protein.
   e. tertiary structure of a protein.

8. Amino acids contain which of the following functional groups?
   1. an NH$_2$ group
   2. an "R" group
   3. glycerol
   4. a COOH group
   5. fatty acid
      a. 1,2,4
      b. 3,5,
      c. 1,2,3
      d. 1,5
      e. 3,4,

9. Peptide bonds are found in _____ while ester linkages are the bonds in _____ .
   a. lipids/proteins
   b. polysaccharides/nucleic acids
   c. proteins/lipids
   d. nucleic acids/polysaccharides
   e. proteins/polysaccharides

10. Lactose and sucrose are examples of
    a. DNA.
    b. monosaccharides.
    c. proteins.
    d. polysaccharides.
    e. disaccharides.

11. The carbon to hydrogen to oxygen ratio of carbohydrates is
    a. very large.
    b. 1:2:1.
    c. 1:2:2.
    d. 2:1:4.
    e. impossible to determine.

12. DNA differs from RNA in that DNA has
    1. two strands.
    2. deoxyribose.
    3. one strand.
    4. ribose.
    5. thymine.
    6. uracil.

    a. 1,2,4
    b. 3,4,6
    c. 2 only
    d. 1,2,5
    e. 1,2,6

13. Lipids that contain unsaturated fatty acids are usually solids at room temperature.
    a. True
    b. False

14. The backbone of the RNA molecule is composed of alternating units of
    a. ribose and phosphate.
    b. purine and pyrimidine.
    c. deoxyribose and phosphate.
    d. deoxyribose and ribose.
    e. uracil and ribose.

15. In the structure C=O, how many pairs of electrons do carbon and oxygen share?
    a. one
    b. two
    c. three
    d. four
    e. five

16. Phospholipids
    a. have a polar and a nonpolar end.
    b. are found in cell membranes.
    c. function as cellular enzymes.
    d. are found only in prokaryotic cells.
    e. Two of the above are correct.

17. What type of bond is formed between the oxygen and the hydrogen atoms in a water molecule?
    a. nonpolar covalent bond
    b. ionic bond
    c. polar covalent bond
    d. savings bond
    e. hydrogen bond

Use the choices on the right to identify the molecules described on the left.

_____ 18. They are made of multiple (CH_2O) units.

_____ 19. They contain COOH and NH_2 groups.

_____ 20. They contain C, H, and O.

_____ 21. They have alternating sugar and phosphate groups.

_____ 22. They contain glycerol.

a. nucleic acids
b. proteins
c. lipids
d. carbohydrates
e. All of the above
f. None of the above

REVIEW QUESTIONS

1. What properties do macromolecules share?

2. Water is essential for life. What properties of water make it so critical for life? How are these properties related to the structure of water?

3. List the macromolecules in order of their importance to cells? Why is this so difficult?

NOTES

3 *FUNCTIONAL ANATOMY OF PROKARYOTES AND EUKARYOTES*

This chapter compares and contrasts the functional anatomy of prokaryotic and eukaryotic cell types. The emphasis is on the prokaryotic cell as represented by the bacteria. The functional anatomy consists of a description of the structure and function of various cellular components. Differences between prokaryotic and eukaryotic cellular structures serve as the basis for the selective action of certain antibiotics. Prokaryotic organisms also have several unique structures as well as a metabolically inactive endospore.

KEY CONCEPTS

1. The effectiveness of a microscope is based on its ability to visually separate two objects that are close together.
2. The many different microscopes that have been developed differ primarily in their lenses and their method of illuminating the specimen being studied.
3. All bacteria must be able to carry out the functions required for life and their small cells must therefore contain the structures to carry out these functions.
4. The composition of the rigid bacterial cell wall determines various properties of the organism, including its susceptibility to penicillin and its staining characteristics.
5. The cytoplasmic membrane largely determines what material gets into and out of the cell.
6. In bacteria, DNA occurs as a covalently closed, circular molecule without a surrounding membrane.
7. The structure of ribosomes differs in eukaryotic and prokaryotic cells; for this reason, some antibacterial medicines such as streptomycin, kill bacteria but are harmless for human cells.
8. Some bacteria can develop into endospores, a type of cell that can survive adverse conditions such as high temperatures.

SUMMARY

I. Microscope Techniques: Instruments
    A. The simple microscope has one magnifying lens.
    B. The compound microscope has two sets of magnifying lenses, the objective lens and the ocular lens. The magnification is the product of the magnification of the individual lenses.
        1. Resolving power determines the usefulness of a microscope, and the amount of detail that can be seen. It depends on the wavelength of the illuminating material.
    C. The contrast between cells and surrounding medium must be increased to clearly see bacteria.
    D. Types of microscopes
        1. Phase contrast microscope—a light microscope that increases the contrast between the bacteria and the surrounding medium.
        2. Interference microscope—the specimen is viewed in three dimensions.
        3. Darkfield microscope—the object being viewed is brightly illuminated against a dark background.
        4. Fluorescence microscope—objects that fluoresce are visualized by this light microscope.
        5. The electron microscope can resolve objects a thousand times better than the light microscope because it uses electrons rather than light to illuminate the specimen.
            a. Specimens must be prepared for viewing in the electron microscope. Such preparation includes fixation, freeze-etching, and thin sectioning.
            b. The scanning electron microscope sees surface details in a three-dimensional image.
            c. The scanning tunneling microscope also views surface structures of specimens but its resolving power is much greater than the electron microscope. Individual atoms can be seen.

II. Microscope Techniques: Staining
    A. Simple staining procedures involve a single dye.
    B. Positive stains color cell components, whereas negative stains do not penetrate the cell.

    C. Differential staining techniques make use of a combination of dyes.
        1. The Gram stain divides bacteria into two groups based upon their cell wall composition: Gram-positive and Gram-negative.
        2. The acid-fast stain is used on members of the genus *Mycobacterium*, which cause tuberculosis and leprosy.
        3. Specific cell structures can be stained by using special techniques that depend on the structure of the material being stained.

III. Shapes of Bacteria
    A. Bacteria have three major shapes: cylindrical, or bacillus; spherical, or coccus; and spiral or spirillum.
    B. Individual cells, especially cocci, may remain attached to one another, forming particular arrangements that are useful in identifying genera.

IV. Functions Required in Prokaryotic and Eukaryotic Cells
    A. All cells must carry out the following functions:
        1. Enclose the internal contents of cell;
        2. replicate genetic information;
        3. synthesize cellular components; and
        4. generate, store, and utilize energy-rich compounds.
    B. In addition, some cells can move, transfer genetic information, store reserve materials, and form a new cell type, the endospore.

V. Enclosure of Cytoplasm in Bacteria
    A. The cytoplasm is enclosed by three layers: the capsule, cell wall, and cytoplasmic membrane.
    B. Capsule, or slime layer
        1. Some cells synthesize a capsule, or slime layer, when growing under certain nutritional conditions. Most capsules are composed of polysaccharides. They are protective to the cell and help attach bacteria to a variety of surfaces.
    C. Cell wall
        1. The bacterial cell wall has several important functions for the cell and its composition confers important properties on it. The cell wall holds a cell together and gives the cell its shape.
        2. The unique structure in all bacterial cell walls that confers rigidity is glycan, which consists of repeating subunits of *N*-acetylglucosamine joined to *N*-acetylmuramic acid, joined to other glycan layers by amino acid bridges. Each layer is termed a peptidoglycan layer.
        3. Cell walls of Gram-positive bacteria consist of multiple layers of peptidoglycan, whereas cell walls of Gram-negative bacteria consist of a single layer of peptidoglycan with several other additional layers. These include lipoprotein, lipopolysaccharide, and phospholipid.
        4. Archaebacteria have no peptidoglycan in their cell walls.
        5. Differences in cell wall composition account for the Gram-staining properties and the effectiveness of penicillin.
    D. Cytoplasmic membrane
    All cells, both prokaryotic and eukaryotic, have a cytoplasmic membrane that determines which molecules enter and leave the cell.
        1. Chemical composition. The cytoplasmic membrane is composed of lipoprotein and phospholipids.
        2. Structure—the cytoplasmic membrane is a bilayer membrane.
        3. Functions—in bacteria, the cytoplasmic membrane is the site of enzymes of energy generation; it controls the exit and entrance of molecules by the mechanisms of diffusion and active transport.
        4. In eukaryotic cells, it forms a series of membranes called the endoplasmic reticulum. Other internal membranes surround structures such as lysosomes and the Golgi apparatus.

VI. Generation of Energy in Eukaryotic Cells
    A. Energy is generated by mitochondria and chloroplasts. Both organelles originated from bacteria that were engulfed by a primitive eukaryotic cell.

VII. Cell Movement
    A. The major structures responsible for movement in all cells are flagella.
    B. Flagella have a relatively simple structure in bacteria. They consist of three parts: filament, hook, and basal body.
    C. Flagella push bacteria which swim through liquids.
        1. Bacteria move toward food sources and away from harmful materials, the process of chemotaxis.
        2. Chemotaxis is a primitive nervous response and operates by determining the length of time the bacteria swim in one direction.
    D. In eukaryotic cells, the structure of flagella in eukaryotic cells is more complex than in bacteria. Flagella move in a whiplike motion to push or pull the cells.

VIII. Cell Attachment
    A. Pili are protein appendages of attachment.

IX. Storage of Genetic Information
    A. The major structure in which the genetic information of all cells is stored is the chromosome.
    B. The bacterial chromosome is a long, double-stranded, circular DNA molecule.
        1. In prokaryotic cells only one or several chromosomes are present per cell and it is not surrounded by a nuclear membrane.
        2. Basic proteins are bound to the DNA.
    C. Plasmids are small DNA molecules that code for nonessential information and replicate independently of the chromosome.
    D. In eukaryotic cells, genetic information is contained in numerous chromosomes, each of which carries different information.
        1. Each DNA strand is composed of double-stranded DNA wound around basic proteins making up a structure called chromatin.
        2. The nucleus also contains the nucleolus, which plays a role in synthesis of ribosomes.

X. Synthesis of Protein
    A. Ribosomes are structures on which proteins are synthesized.
        1. Ribosomes are composed of ribosomal protein and ribosomal RNA.
        2. Eukaryotic ribosomes differ from prokaryotic ribosomes in that they contain different proteins and RNA, and also differ in weight.
    B. Many antibiotics inhibit the correct functioning of prokaryotic ribosomes without affecting eukaryotic ribosomes.

XI. Storage Materials
    A. Bacteria often store a variety of materials that they later use as a source of nutrients. These include glycogen, volutin, and ß-hydroxybutyric acid.

XII. Endospores
    A. The endospore is a unique cell type that develops from actively multiplying cells (vegetative cells) when they face starvation.
    B. Endospores have unusual staining and resistance properties.
    C. Many endospore-producing bacteria cause disease.

TERMS AND DEFINITIONS

1. Along with actin _____ are protein filaments that comprise a network or internal skeleton

   within the eukaryotic cell known as the _____ .

2. The _____ is a microscope that has two sets of magnifying lenses. These

   lenses are the _____ and the _____ .

3. Another name for membrane transport proteins that function to facilitate the movement of small molecules into and out of the cell is _____ .

4. _____ is the process of division by most bacteria in which one cell divides to form two identical daughter cells.

5. The phenomenon of flagellated bacteria moving toward a nutrient source or away from harmful materials is called _____ .

6. _____ are the toxic lipid portions of the lipopolysaccharides of Gram-negative bacteria.

7. Bacterial cells that retain the primary dye after decolorizing in the Gram staining procedure are said to be Gram- _____ .

8. _____ are membrane-bound organelles in eukaryotic cells that contain very powerful digestive enzymes.

9. The differential staining procedure used to identify the causative agents of tuberculosis and leprosy is the _____ stain.

10. _____ is a macromolecule found only in the cell wall of most eubacteria.

11. Circular, double-stranded bits of DNA that are not part of the bacterial chromosome, are only a fraction of its size, and are not, except under certain conditions, essential for the survival of the cell are called _____ .

12. Bacterial flagella anchor into the cell wall and membrane by means of the _____ .

13. The capsule, the cell wall, and the cytoplasmic membrane are collectively referred to as the cell _____ .

14. Archaebacteria found in the Great Salt Lake are described as "salt loving" cells or _____ .

15. The _____ power of a microscope is a measure of its ability to separate small details.

Match the microscope from the list on the right with its description on the left.

_____ 16. Has optical devices to increase contrast between specimen and the background.
_____ 17. Allows a 3-dimensional view of an object's surface.
_____ 18. Visualizes objects that emit light when light of a different wavelength strikes the object.
_____ 19. Produces a map of the bumps and valleys of the atoms on the surface of a sample.
_____ 20. Uses two beams of light to produce a 3-dimensional appearance.
_____ 21. Objects appear bright against a dark background.
_____ 22. Electrons rather than light pass through the specimen.

a. phase contrast microscope
b. fluorescence microscope
c. scanning tunneling microscope
d. darkfield microscope
e. transmission electron microscope
f. interference microscopes
g. scanning electron microscope

SELF-TEST OF READING MATERIAL

1. *Streptococcus mutans*, the major organism causing dental caries, attaches to the surface of teeth by a polysaccharide capsule. This capsule is synthesized only from
    a. diaminopimelic acid.
    b. sucrose.
    c. amino acids.
    d. glucose.
    e. lipid.

2. The cell wall of Gram-positive bacteria is composed primarily of
    a. chitin.
    b. cellulose.
    c. starch.
    d. protein.
    e. peptidoglycan.

3. Which of the following is essential for living cells?
    a. pili
    b. flagella
    c. cell wall
    d. cytoplasmic membrane
    e. capsule

4. Which of the following would contain peptidoglycan?
    1. ribosomes
    2. Gram-positive cell walls
    3. pili
    4. cytoplasmic membrane
    5. flagella
    6. Gram-negative cell walls

    a. 1 only
    b. 1,4
    c. 2,3,4
    d. 2 only
    e. 2,6

5. The process of cellular differentiation that produces an endospore from a vegetative cell is
    a. germination.
    b. common among the bacilli.
    c. sporogenesis.
    d. common among the cocci.
    e. Two of the above are correct.

6. In bacteria, sterols would be found only in the cell membranes of
    a. *Mycoplasma.*
    b. viruses.
    c. *Bacillus.*
    d. *Mycobacterium.*
    e. Sterols are never found in bacteria.

7. The group of bacteria that do not have cell walls are the
    a. archaebacteria.
    b. mycoplasma.
    c. eubacteria.
    d. mycobacteria.
    e. Both a and d are correct.

8. Cells that do not have a membrane separating their nuclear material from their cytoplasm are called
    a. heterozygous.
    b. prokaryotic.
    c. homozygous.
    d. eukaryotic.
    e. viruses.

9. Which of the following structures is unique to prokaryotic organisms?
    a. mitochondria
    b. ribosomes
    c. cell wall
    d. peptidoglycan cell wall
    e. cell membrane

10. Cell membranes are composed primarily of
    a. protein and polysaccharides.
    b. protein and phospholipid.
    c. phospholipid and polysaccharide.
    d. peptidoglycan in prokaryotes.
    e. Both b and d are correct.

11. Which of the following components are not found in the Gram-positive cell wall?
    a. lipopolysaccharides
    b. peptidoglycan
    c. teichoic acid
    d. N-acetyl muramic acid
    e. amino acids

12. Spherical bacteria arranged in a chain are known as
    a. spirochetes.
    b. bacilli.
    c. staphylococci.
    d. streptobacilli.
    e. streptococci.

13. Which of the following structures are known to protect bacteria from phagocytosis by white blood cells?
    a. flagella
    b. endospore
    c. capsule
    d. lister body
    e. ribosomes

14. Bacterial flagella and the flagella of eukaryotic cells have the same function but differ considerably in their structure.
    a. True
    b. False

15. Endotoxins are
    1. found in gram positive cells.
    2. lipopolysaccharides.
    3. found in Gram-negative cells.
    4. lipoproteins.
    5. found in *Mycoplasma.*
    a. 1,2,5
    b. 1,2
    c. 2,3
    d. 3,4
    e. 3,4,5

16. Encapsulated bacteria
    a. are sometimes more virulent than their non-encapsulated counterparts.
    b. are "time-released" and easier to swallow than tablet bacteria.
    c. are more susceptible to phagocytic destruction.
    d. have more fun than non-encapsulated bacteria.
    e. Both a and c are correct.

17. Bacterial flagella impart motility to the cell by
    a. undulating movement.
    b. rotary movement.
    c. gliding.
    d. a and b.
    e. b and c.

REVIEW QUESTIONS

1. What are the two most important functions of a microscope?

2. List four essential life functions that all cells must have.

3. Why are penicillin and streptomycin active against bacteria but are not active against human cells?

4. List three ways in which endospores differ from vegetative cells.

ANSWERS:
   Terms and Definitions
      1. microtubules/cytoskeleton 2. compound microscope/objective/ocular 3. permeases 4. binary fission
      5. chemotaxis 6. endotoxins 7. positive 8. lysosomes 9. acid-fast 10. peptidoglycan 11. plasmids
      12. basal body 13. envelope 14. halophilic 15. resolving 16. a 17. g 18. b 19. c 20. f 21. d 22. e
   Self-Test of Reading Material
      1. b 2.e 3. d 4. e 5. c 6. a 7. b 8. b 9. d 10. b 11. a 12. e 13. c 14. a 15. c 16. a 17. b

NOTES

4 DYNAMICS OF BACTERIAL GROWTH

This chapter describes how microorganisms grow. Microorganisms are under the influence of the same factors that control the growth of any other organism. However, microorganisms do have some unique features in their growth patterns and their small size presents certain problems in measuring their growth. Bacteria multiply by binary fission in which one cell produces two identical daughter cells. When we describe the growth of bacteria we talk of the growth of populations rather than of individuals. This chapters explores the factors that affect the growth of mircoorganisms and describes how these factors often determine the habitat in which an organism grows.

KEY CONCEPTS

1. Bacterial growth is measured by an increase in cell numbers; growth of most other organisms is measured by an increase in their size.
2. All bacteria require a source of carbon to synthesize components of cytoplasm as well as a source of energy in order to grow. Different bacteria use different materials for their nutrients.
3. The growth requirements of bacteria may change permanently when they are taken from their natural environment and are grown in the laboratory.
4. Representatives of different groups of bacteria can multiply over a very broad range of environmental and nutritional conditions.
5. Bacteria are often able to alter their internal environment to compensate for changes in the external environment.

SUMMARY

I. Pure Culture Methods
    A. In nature, bacteria exist as a mixed population.
    B. Colonies represent the offspring of a single cell, and the streak plate method is used to separate cells.
    C. The properties of agar make it ideal for growing bacteria on a solid surface.

II. Measurement of Cell Growth
    A. Bacterial growth is defined in terms of population size, not by size of individual cells.
        1. Bacteria divide by binary fission.
        2. Number of bacteria increases exponentially.
    B. There are several methods for measuring bacterial growth.
        1. Scattering of light measures living and dead cells.
        2. Growth can be measured as an increase in cell number.
            a. Plate count measures number of viable cells that can grow into a colony.
            b. Direct microscopic count is rapid but does not distinguish between living and dead bacteria.

III. Multiplication of Microorganisms—General Aspects
    A. Microorganisms multiply under an enormous range of environmental conditions.
    B. An organism taken from its natural habitat often shows altered growth requirements when grown in the laboratory.

IV. Factors Influencing Microbial Growth
   A.   Environmental factors that influence growth include temperature, oxygen, pH, and osmotic pressure.
      1.   Temperature of growth. Most bacteria grow within a temperature range of approximately 30°C.
         a.   Psychrophiles—optimum growth temperature is between -5° and 20°C.
         b.   Mesophiles—optimum growth temperature is between 20° and 50°C.
         c.   Thermophiles—optimum growth temperature is between 50° and 80°C.
         d.   Extreme thermophiles—optimum growth temperature is above 80°C.
      2.   Oxygen requirements for growth.
         a.   Obligate (strict) aerobes have an absolute requirement for oxygen.
         b.   Obligate (strict) anaerobes cannot multiply if oxygen is present, since it kills bacteria.
         c.   Facultative anaerobes can utilize oxygen if it is available but can grow, although less well, in its absence.
         d.   Microaerophilic organisms require small amounts of oxygen (2%–10%) but higher concentrations are toxic.
         e.   Aerotolerant organisms grow in the presence or absence of oxygen, but they derive no benefit from the oxygen.
      3.   Aerobes require oxygen because they have metabolic pathways that require oxygen to convert energy in foodstuffs into forms useful to the cell.
         a.   Bacteria that require oxygen have the means to detoxify toxic forms of oxygen, such as hydrogen peroxide.
         b.   Detoxifying enzymes include catalase and superoxide dismutase.
      4.   Most bacteria grow best in a medium with a pH 7 (neutral).
         a.   Buffers are added to media to maintain a constant pH.
         b.   Bacteria can maintain their internal contents at neutral pH even though the external pH is below or above this.
      5.   Osmotic pressure is determined by the concentration of dissolved substances in the medium in which bacteria are growing.
         a.   Under normal conditions, the osmotic pressure is slightly higher on the inside than on the outside of the cell.
         b.   Bacteria can compensate for pressure differences to a certain extent if the external osmotic pressure is high.

V.   Nutritional Aspects of Bacterial Growth
   A.   Cell multiplication requires a source of energy and raw materials for synthesis of cell components.
      1.   Spectrum of nutritional types:
         a.   Photoautotrophs use light (radiant) energy and CO_2 as a source of carbon.
         b.   Photoheterotrophs use light (radiant) energy and organic compounds as a source of carbon.
         c.   Chemoautotrophs use chemical energy and CO_2 as a source of carbon.
         d.   Chemoheterotrophs use chemical energy and organic compounds as a source of carbon.
         e.   Lithoheterotrophs use an inorganic source of energy and organic compounds as a source of carbon.
      2.   All organisms require a supply of nitrogen, sulfur, and phosphorous.
      3.   Growth factors:
         a.   Bacteria require small molecules that serve as subunits of biosynthetic macromolecules and cell components.
         b.   Some bacteria can synthesize all of their growth factors; others that lack the necessary biosynthetic enzymes must have them provided.

VI. Cultivation of Bacteria in the Laboratory
   A.   The two kinds of media on which bacteria are grown are synthetic (defined) or complex (undefined) media.
      1.   Synthetic medium consists of chemically pure materials added in known amounts.
      2.   Complex (undefined) medium consists of undefined nutrients such as ground meat, added in known amounts.

VII. Problems Associated with Growth of Microorganisms in the Laboratory
    A. No single medium has been devised on which all bacteria will grow. This may result from several factors:
        1. Toxic compounds may be present and must be removed.
        2. Unusual growth factors may be needed.
        3. Some bacteria can only be grown in mixed culture, similar to their natural environment. One bacterium provides what the other one needs.
    B. Anaerobes require special cultivation methods.
        1. An anaerobe jar may be used to remove all oxygen.
        2. Chemicals may be added to react with the oxygen.

VIII. Cultivation of Organisms that Occur as a Minor Part of the Microbial Population
    A. Enrichment cultures enhance the growth of specific organisms.
    B. Selective media preferentially inhibit the growth of certain organisms.

IX. Dynamics of Bacterial Population Growth—Four Well-recognized Phases
    A. Lag phase of growth involves no increase in cell numbers—the "tooling-up" phase.
    B. Exponential phase of growth is the time during which cell number increases exponentially.
    C. Stationary phase is reached when the numbers of viable cells stops increasing.
    D. Death phase is characterized by an exponential decrease in the number of viable cells.

X. Growth of a Bacterial Colony
    A. Colony enlargement results from cells multiplying at the outside edges of the colony.

XI. Growth of Bacteria in Nature
    A. In the laboratory, bacteria grow in a closed system; nutrients are not renewed and waste products are not removed.
    B. An open system is the typical system found in nature. Nutrients are replenished and waste products are removed.
        1. A chemostat in the laboratory simulates an open system in nature.
        2. The doubling time as well as the population size of bacteria can be controlled by a chemostat.

TERMS AND DEFINITIONS

1. _____ are added to bacterial growth media to prevent the accumulation of acid byproducts.

2. The time required for one cell to divide into two is the doubling time or _____ .

3. _____ is a polysaccharide extracted from marine algae and used as a solidifying agent in bacterial media.

4. A medium that contains substances to inhibit the growth of unwanted microorganisms is called

   a _____ medium.

5. _____ are small organic molecules, other than energy sources, that must be provided to bacteria in order to grow.

6. A medium for the growth of nutritionally demanding bacteria is enriched with blood and carefully heated to release the

   growth factor hematin is called _____ .

7. When one cell divides and forms two identical daughter cell the process is called _____ .

Match the category of organism from the list on the right with its description on the left. Some descriptions may have more than one answer and may be used more than once.

_____ 8. A bacterium with an optimal growth temperature of 37°C.

_____ 9. A yeast that grows in the presence or absence of oxygen.

_____ 10. A bacterium isolated from the intestines of an Arctic cod that is killed when exposed to the air.

_____11. A mold that dies when incubated in an air-tight container.

_____12. An oxygen-dependent bacterium growing in boiling hot springs in Yellowstone National Park.

_____13. Usually must be grown in a candle jar because they cannot tolerate oxygen levels above 10%.

_____14. *E. coli* that grows in our intestines.

_____15. A bacterium with an optimal growth temperature of 62°C.

a. psychrophile
b. obligate aerobe
c. thermophile
d. facultative anaerobe
e. mesophile
f. microaerophile
g. extreme thermophile
h. obligate anaerobe

SELF-TEST OF READING MATERIAL

1. Photoautotrophic metabolism involves
   1. the use of inorganic carbon dioxide as the sole source of carbon.
   2. sunlight as the source of energy.
   3. "rock eaters."
   4. the use of organic carbon compounds as a source of carbon.
   5. energy derived from the oxidation of inorganic or organic molecules.

   a. 1,2
   b. 1,2,3
   c. 3,4,5
   d. 4,5
   e. 3 only

2. Bacteria observed multiplying in the Dead Sea are most likely to be
   a. psychrophiles.
   b. anaerobic.
   c. mesophiles.
   d. halophiles.
   e. thermophiles.

3. Which of the following is essential for the growth of all bacteria?
   a. vitamins
   b. oxygen
   c. water
   d. glucose
   e. phospholipids

4. An organism that can grow either in the presence or in the absence of molecular oxygen is called a(n)
   a. obligate aerobe.
   b. facultative anaerobe.
   c. obligate anaerobe.
   d. facultative aerobe.
   e. halophile.

5. Cells make coenzymes from
   a. enzymes.
   b. carbohydrates.
   c. vitamins.
   d. proteins.
   e. apoenzymes.

6. Bacteria isolated from Antarctic marine fish are probably
   a. psychrophiles.
   b. mesophiles.
   c. halophiles.
   d. rockfordfiles.
   e. Both a and c are correct.

7. An 18-hour broth culture of *E. coli* contains

   a. *E. coli* cells that are all dividing exponentially.
   b. *E. coli* cells that dividing at the same rate.
   c. mostly endospores.
   d. *E. coli* cells that are all in stationary growth phase.
   e. *E. coli* cells that are in all phases of growth.

Use the following curve to answer questions 8 through 12.

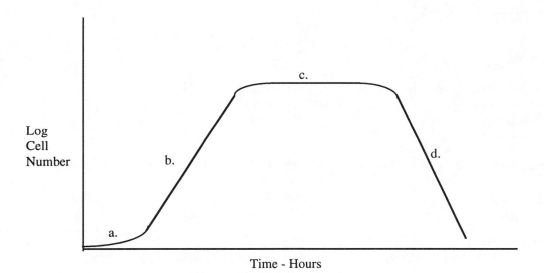

Time - Hours

_____ 8. During this phase of growth, bacteria in a population are adjusting to their medium.

_____ 9. During this phase of growth, bacteria are growing exponentially.

_____ 10. During this phase of growth, the bacterial population is doubling at a constant rate.

_____ 11. During this phase of growth, bacteria are dying exponentially.

_____ 12. During this phase of growth, cell division is equal to cell death.

13. Bacteria with an optimum growth temperature around 10°C are called
    a. thermophiles.
    b. mesophiles.
    c. acidophiles.
    d. psychopathic.
    e. psychrophiles.

14. The best definition of the generation time of a bacterial population is the
    a. time it takes for a bacterial population to double.
    b. time it takes for the lag phase.
    c. length of the exponential phase.
    d. time it takes for nuclear division.
    e. maximum rate of doubling.

15. A chemoheterotroph would use which of the following as a source of carbon?
    a. inorganic carbon
    b. carbon dioxide
    c. carbonate
    d. vitamins
    e. glucose

16. A bacterial culture began with 4 cells and ended with 128 cells. How many generations did the population go through?
    a. 64
    b. 32
    c. 6
    d. 5
    e. 4

17. Fungi generally grow best at a pH around
    a. 1.
    b. 5.
    c. 7.
    d. 9.
    e. 14.

18. Bacterial broth cultures eventually stop growing and enter stationary phase because they
    a. deplete an essential nutrient.
    b. accumulate toxic products.
    c. become too crowded.
    d. Both a and b.
    e. Both a and c.

19. Which of the following could be added to a culture medium to neutralize acids and keep the pH near neutrality?
    a. buffers
    b. sugars
    c. agar
    d. heat
    e. water

20. A facultative anaerobic organism
    a. doesn't use oxygen, but is not killed by it.
    b. is killed by oxygen.
    c. grows in the presence or absence of oxygen.
    d. requires less oxygen than is present in air.
    e. prefers to grow without oxygen.

21. Agar is a good agent for solidifying liquid media because it
    a. is a good nutrient source.
    b. is a seaweed.
    c. liquefies at 40°C.
    d. solidifies around 100°C.
    e. is metabolized by very few bacteria.

22. Most bacteria grow best at pH:
    a. 1.
    b. 5.
    c. 7.
    d. 9.
    e. 14.

REVIEW QUESTIONS

1. Complete the following table.

NUTRITIONAL TYPE	SOURCE OF ENERGY	SOURCE OF CARBON
PHOTOAUTOTROPHS		
PHOTOHETEROTROPHS		
CHEMOAUTOTROPHS		
CHEMOHETEROTROPHS		

2. Describe the four stages of growth of a bacterial population in a broth medium.

3. Give an example of an environment from which you might isolate (a) a thermophile, (b) a mesophile, (c) a psychrophile.

4. Distinguish between a selective and a differential medium.

NOTES

ANSWERS:
  Terms and Definitions
   1. buffers 2. generation time 3. agar 4. selective 5. growth factors 6. chocolate agar 7. binary fission 8. e
   9. d 10. a,h 11. b 12. b,g 13. f 14. d,e 15. c
  Self-Test of Reading Material
   1. a 2. d 3. c 4. b 5. c 6. a 7. e 8. a 9. b 10. b 11. d 12. c 13. e 14. a 15. e 16. d 17. b 18. d 19. a
   20. c 21. e 22. c

5 *METABOLISM: THE GENERATION OF ENERGY AND SYNTHESIS OF SMALL MOLECULES*

As an essential function of life, organisms take in nutrient molecules; degrade them to generate energy and smaller molecules; then, using the energy, they reassemble these small molecules to meet their own needs. This very basic process of life is known as metabolism. This chapter focuses on the catabolic portion of metabolism during which nutrient molecules are broken down to generate energy and small molecules. These products of catabolism are then available for reassembly. Respiration and fermentation are the processes by which the cell accomplishes both the generation of energy and of small molecules. Many of these small molecules can be used for identification of bacterial species. The chapter ends with a look at some other ways in which microorganisms generate energy.

KEY CONCEPTS

1. Cells must carry out two metabolic functions: 1) degrade foodstuffs to generate energy and small molecules, and 2) use the energy to convert the small molecules into marcomolecules and cell structures.
2. Foodstuffs are degraded by two major pathways: respiration or fermentation.
3. Respiration produces much more energy than fermentation for the same amount of foodstuff degraded.
4. The tricarboxylic acid cycle has two functions: 1) to produce energy, and 2) to synthesize compounds that are converted into amino acids.
5. Bacteria as a group have a wide variety of enzymes and synthesize a large number of different products. Identifying these end products can help identify the different species of bacteria.

SUMMARY

I. Overview
   A. To multiply, cells must degrade (catabolize) foodstuffs to gain energy. Foodstuffs also serve as a source of precursor metabolites for the synthesis of subunits of macromolecules. The synthesis of cell components (anabolism) requires energy.

II. Enzymes—Chemical Kinetics and Mechanism of Action
   A. Enzymes rearrange atoms under the mild conditions of temperature and pressure at which cells can live.
   B. Enzymes speed up reactions by lowering their activation energy.
   C. The shape of the substrate must fit the shape of the enzyme that acts on it.
      1. An enzyme functions by combining with its substrate through weak bonding forces. Next, the products of the reaction are released, leaving the enzymes unchanged.
   D. Environmental and chemical factors influence enzyme activity.
      1. Important features of the environment include temperature, pH, and salt concentration.
         a. A 10°C rise in temperature doubles the speed of enzymatic reactions.
         b. Most enzymes function best near a pH of 7.
      2. Enzymes are inhibited by a variety of compounds that may result in a reversible or irreversible inhibition. An example of reversible inhibition is sulfa drugs, which compete with para-aminobenzoic acid for the active site of an enzyme used to synthesize the vitamin folic acid. An irreversible inhibitor may alter amino acids that give the enzyme its shape.

III. Energy Metabolism
- A. One of the pathways of energy metabolism involves the enzymatic conversion of a large number of low-energy bonds to a few high-energy bonds from which ATP, the storage form of energy, can be synthesized.
- B. The two major pathways for generating energy are fermentation, in which an organic compound is the final hydrogen acceptor, and respiration, in which an inorganic compound is the final hydrogen acceptor.
- C. Both pathways also generate precursor metabolites for the synthesis of cell components. Respiration, but not fermentation, produces reducing power.
- D. Glycolysis is the most common pathway for degrading sugars.
  - 1. A glucose molecule metabolized through the glycolytic pathway results in the production of 2 molecules of ATP, 2 molecules of pyruvic acid, and 2 molecules of NADH.
  - 2. The pyruvic acid is metabolized to different compounds depending on the species of bacterium and whether or not oxygen is present. (a) If oxygen is not present, pyruvate is converted to a variety of products, using the NADH generated in glycolysis. These include: (1) lactic acid in lactic acid fermentation, (2) alcohol and CO_2 in the alcoholic fermentation and (3) a variety of other compounds in a mixed fermentation.

IV. Energy Metabolism—Respiration
- A. The TCA cycle oxidizes pyruvic acid to CO_2 and H_2O, and then traps the energy of pyruvic acid in ATP.
  - 1. Carbon skeleton transformation—The acetyl CoA is converted to 2 molecules of citric acid, which is converted to 2 molecules of CO_2, and 4 NADH molecules in every turn of the TCA cycle.
  - 2. Energy transformations—The electrons for the hydrogen atoms removed in the reactions are transferred through the electron transport chain, which generates the high-energy bonds of ATP. This process is called oxidative phosphorylation.
- B. Much more energy is gained in respiration than in fermentation.
  - 1. About 20 times more energy is gained if glucose is oxidized completely to CO_2 and H_2O, rather than if its metabolism stops at pyruvic acid.

V. Respiration Under Anaerobic Conditions
- A. Some bacteria can utilize other inorganic compounds besides oxygen as electron acceptors. The most common acceptors are nitrate, sulfate, and carbon dioxide. Less ATP is generated compared to aerobic respiration.

VI. Metabolism of Compounds Other than Glucose
- A. Some bacteria have pathways other than the glycolytic pathway.

VII. Other Pathways of Glucose Degradation
- A. Entner-Doudoroff Pathway
- B. Pentose-phosphate pathway provides reducing power for biosynthesis as well as certain precursor metabolites.

VIII. Oxidation of Inorganic Compounds
- A. Some bacteria can oxidize a variety of inorganic compounds to gain energy.

IX. Biosynthetic Metabolism
- A. Degradative and biosynthetic pathways may be part of the same pathway.
  - 1. Degradative pathways generate the compounds that serve as starting materials for the synthesis of cell components.
- B. Many amino acids are synthesized from the same precursor metabolites.
- C. A very important reaction in biosynthetic metabolism is the mechanism by which NH_4^+ is incorporated into organic compounds. An especially important reaction is the addition of NH_4^+ to α-ketoglutaric acid to form glutamic acid. This reaction is reversible and connects anabolism with catabolism. The NH_4^+ can be transferred to a variety of other α-keta acids to form other amino acids.
- D. Purines and pyrimidines are synthesized stepwise along different pathways.

X.   Bacterial Photosynthesis
   A.   Light energy absorbed by chlorophyll provides energy to reduce CO_2 to cell material.
   B.   Compounds other than H_2O serve as the reducing agent in photosynthetic bacteria other than cyanobacteria.
      1.   If oxygen is released, then photosynthesis is termed oxygenic; if it is not released, it is termed anoxygenic.
   C.   Photosynthesis requires light for energy generation but biosynthetic reactions do not.
      1.   "Light" reactions only occur in photosynthetic organisms that gain energy from light. Electrons are transferred along an electron transport chain and ATP is generated in the process.
      2.   "Dark" reactions. Actually, formation of carbohydrate can occur in light or dark. A key reaction is the addition of CO_2 to the 5-carbon compound ribulose 1, 5-biphosphate to form a metabolite in the glycolytic pathway. This compound is converted to cell components.

TERMS AND DEFINITIONS

1.   Synthetic compounds that are very difficult if not impossible for microorganisms to degrade are

   called _____ .

2.   _____ is the universal currency of energy in cells.

3.   _____ are organic molecules that are converted into products by enzymatic reactions to become subunits of macromolecules.

4.   Energy that must be supplied to a chemical reaction in order to get it going is called the

   energy of _____ .

5.   _____ is the addition of electrons or hydrogen atoms to a molecule.

6.   The process in cells that involves the oxidation of glucose to pyruvic acid with the production of 2 ATP

   is known as _____ .

7.   Sulfa drugs act on bacterial cells by _____ inhibition.

8.   _____ and _____ are electron carriers in the electron transport system.

9.   The removal of electrons or hydrogen atoms from a molecule is called _____ .

10.   _____ are small, non-protein molecules that function in the transfer of atoms from one molecule to another.

11.   The point at which a substrate attaches to its specific enzyme is called the _____ or the

   _____ site.

SELF-TEST OF READING MATERIAL

1. During aerobic respiration, the final hydrogen acceptor molecule is
   a. an organic compound.
   b. pyruvic acid.
   c. oxygen.
   d. cytochrome.
   e. glucose.

2. Reduction is the
   a. addition of protons.
   b. removal of electrons.
   c. addition of oxygen.
   d. removal of electrons or hydrogen atoms.
   e. addition of electrons or hydrogen atoms.

3. The amount of ATP synthesized during aerobic respiration is
   a. much less than that from fermentation.
   b. greater than that from fermentation.
   c. about the same as that from fermentation.

4. The catalytic activity of an enzyme is determined by the
   a. substrate.
   b. presence of ions.
   c. 3-dimensional shape of the enzyme.
   d. presence of vitamins.
   e. hydrolysis of ATP.

5. What is the net gain of ATP from the oxidation of glucose to carbon dioxide and alcohol?
   a. 2
   b. 4
   c. 34
   d. 38
   e. 40

6. Which of the following is not an enzyme?
   a. dehydrogenase
   b. cellulase
   c. coenzyme A
   d. lactase
   e. hexokinase

7. The ATP produced during glycolysis is the result of
   a. substrate phosphorylation.
   b. oxidative reduction.
   c. substrate reduction.
   d. oxidative phosphorylation.
   e. photophosphorylation.

8. Bacteria need energy for
   a. synthesizing macromolecules.
   b. cell division.
   c. motility.
   d. transport of nutrients.
   e. All of the above processes require energy.

9. The synthesis of ATP from ADP and inorganic phosphate in which the source of energy is from the transfer of electrons is called
   a. substrate reduction.
   b. reductive phosphorylation.
   c. substrate oxidation.
   d. photooxidation.
   e. oxidative phosphorylation.

10. The molecules on which enzymes work are called
    a. substrates.
    b. inhibitors.
    c. active molecules.
    d. coenzymes.
    e. ATP.

11. Which of the following competitively inhibits enzyme activity in the synthesis of folic acid?
    a. sulfa drugs
    b. vitamins
    c. penicillin
    d. PABA
    e. folic acid

12. Which of the following would not be a product of fermentation?
    a. acetic acid
    b. ethyl alcohol
    c. carbon dioxide
    d. pyruvic acid
    e. lactic acid

13. Approximately what percent of the energy in a glucose molecule is converted to ATP during aerobic respiration?
    a. 5%
    b. 11%
    c. 50%
    d. 89%
    e. 95%

14. Catalase is the enzyme involved in
    a. substrate phosphorylation.
    b. the synthesis of hydrogen peroxide.
    c. the breakdown of acetoin.
    d. the synthesis of acetoin.
    e. the breakdown of hydrogen peroxide.

15. Anaerobic respiration might use which of the following electron acceptors?
    a. glucose
    b. pyruvate
    c. oxygen
    d. cytochrome
    e. nitrate

16. Oxidation is the
    a. addition of protons.
    b. addition of neutrons.
    c. removal of protons.
    d. removal of electrons or hydrogen atoms.
    e. addition of electrons or hydrogen atoms.

17. Hydrogens removed during the oxidation of glucose are usually transferred to
    a. INS.
    b. ATP.
    c. NAD.
    d. DNA.
    e. ADP.

18. During fermentation, glucose is oxidized to
    a. sugar.
    b. water.
    c. a variety of products depending on the organism.
    d. oxygen.
    e. fermentation is reduction and not oxidation.

19. Enzymes work by supplying the activation energy required for a chemical reaction to take place.
    a. True
    b. False

20. In eukaryotic cells, glycolysis takes place in the mitochondrian.
    a. True
    b. False

REVIEW QUESTIONS

1. Distinguish the following from each other: substrate phosphorylation, oxidative phosphorylation, and photophosphorylation.

2. Complete the following table by indicating the number of molecules of ATP, NADH, and FADH produced from one glucose molecule.

	ATP	NADH	FADH
GLYCOLYSIS			
PYRUVIC ACID TO ACETYL CoA			
TCA CYCLE			

3. Summarize the reactions and products of glycolysis in a single sentence.

4. How do the end products of photosynthesis in cyanobacteria and green plants differ?

ANSWERS:
Terms and Definitions
1. xenobiotics 2. ATP 3. precursor metabolites 4. activation 5. reduction 6. glycolysis 7. competitive 8. cytochromes/quinones 9. oxidation 10. coenzymes 11. active/catalytic
Self-Test of Reading Material
1. c 2. e 3. b 4. c 5. a 6. c 7. a 8. e 9. e 10. a 11. a 12. d 13. c 14. e 15. e 16. d 17. c 18. c 19. b 20. b

6 INFORMATIONAL MOLECULES: FUNCTION, SYNTHESIS, AND REGULATION OF ACTIVITY

In order to reproduce and to carry on the many activities associated with life, cells must have a plan or blueprint to follow. These instructions are carried in the form of a macromolecule called DNA. DNA is an amazing molecule not only because it contains the codes for every life function, but also because it reproduces itself and rarely makes a mistake. In addition to replication, DNA also directs the synthesis of another macromolecule, RNA, that serves as a messenger in the process of protein synthesis. The code for the life is actually a code for the synthesis of proteins. Cells monitor their environment and synthesize only those proteins that are necessary at that particular moment. Cells have a means of control or regulation of their protein synthesis.

KEY CONCEPTS

1. The general rule for the flow of information in cells is:

DNA $\xrightarrow[\text{the synthesis of}]{\text{codes for}}$ RNA $\xrightarrow[\text{amino acids in}]{\text{codes for}}$ Protein

2. In the transfer of information, a sequence of nucleotides in DNA determines a sequence of amino acids in proteins.
3. DNA has two functions: to store genetic information and to reproduce itself.
4. The sequence of nucleotides in one strand of DNA determines the sequence in the other strand.
5. The enzymes of bacteria may change with changes in the environment, because it turns on and turns off gene functions.
6. The synthesis of many small molecules, such as amino acids, is controlled by regulating the activity as well as the number of enzyme molecules involved in the synthesis of the amino acid.
7. Bacteria synthesize only the amounts of each cell component that they need in order to multiply most rapidly.

SUMMARY

I. Chemistry of DNA and RNA
   A. DNA occurs as a double-stranded helix held together by hydrogen bonds between adenine and thymine, and between guanine and cytosine.
   B. The two strands run in opposite direction, one going form the top to the bottom; the other from the bottom to the top.
   C. RNA is usually single-stranded and shorter than DNA.

II. Information Storage and Transfer
   A. Information is stored in DNA and RNA in the sequence of their nucleotide subunits.
   B. Information in DNA can be transferred by two different processes.
      1. The sequence of nucleotides in DNA can be transferred to mRNA, which determines the sequence of amino acids in proteins.
      2. Replication of DNA—This begins at a specific site on the chromosome and proceeds by the sequential addition of nucleotides by DNA polymerase. Two chromosomes identical to the original are formed.

III. Expression of Genes
  A. A bacterial chromosome consists of two major regions. One codes for proteins (coding region); the other determines whether the first region will be expressed (regulatory region).
  B. The sequence of three nucleotides in mRNA determines a specific amino acid, a triplet code.
  C. Gene transcription is the process of making an RNA copy of the genetic information in DNA.
    1. There are three steps in transcription.
        a. Initiation—The sigma factor of RNA polymerase bind to a promoter region in the regulatory region of the gene.
        b. Elongation—RNA polymerase moves along one of the strands of DNA (template strand) synthesizing a complementary single strand of mRNA.
        c. Termination—RNA polymerase comes to a stop signal at the end of a gene and is released.
  D. The second step in gene expression is the translation of mRNA into protein.
    1. The sets of three nucleotides (codons) that code for each amino acid have been identified. Most amino acids have several codons.
    2. Translation involves three steps.
        a. Initiation—The ribosome binds to a region near the beginning of the mRNA to start translation.
        b. Elongation—A charged tRNA molecules attach to its complementary codon of the mRNA positioned at a particular site on the ribosome. The ribosome moves along the mRNA three nucleotides at a time so that another charged tRNA bonds to the next complementary codon. The amino acids are joined together in a peptide bond.
        c. Termination—When the ribosome reaches a stop codon in the mRNA, the protein dissociates from the tRNA, and protein synthesis stops.

IV. Differences Between Prokaryotic and Eukaryotic Gene Transcription/Translation
  A. There are a number of differences.
    1. In prokaryotic cells, transcription and translation occur almost simultaneously; in eukaryotes, mRNA is transported out of the nucleus before translation begins.
    2. In eukaryotes, most mRNA molecules are modified before they are translated. Blocks of nucleotides are cut out, a situation very rare in prokaryotes.

V. The Environment and Control Systems
  A. Bacteria may be subjected to rapidly changing nutrients in the environment. They have the means to shut off or activate pathways of biosynthesis and degradation so as to synthesize only the materials they need in any particular environment.

VI. Mechanisms of Control of Biosynthetic Pathways
  A. End product repression controls the start of gene transcription.
    1. The end product binds to the repressor and changes its shape so that it can then bind to the operator region of the gene. This prevents the RNA from binding to the promoter.
  B. End products control the activity of the first enzyme of the biosynthetic pathway (allosteric control).
    1. The end product combines with the first enzyme of the pathway and changes its shape so that it can no longer catalyze its reaction. The inhibition of the first enzyme shuts down the entire pathway.

VII. Mechanisms of Control of Degradative Pathways
  A. Metabolites that can be degraded activate the genes responsible for their degradation.
    1. The compound to be degraded turns on the pathway that degrade it. The compound binds to the repressor protein and activates it, thereby allowing the RNA polymerase to initiate transcription.
  B. Catabolite repression ensures efficient use of available foodstuffs.
    1. A catabolite repressor can reduce the level of cyclic AMP required for induction of certain pathways, so the catabolite repressor is metabolized first.
  C. Some very important enzymes are synthesized at the same level independent of the medium. These are termed constitutive.

TERMS AND DEFINITIONS

1. The _____ of a gene determines the sequence of amino acids in a polypeptide chain.

2. The subunits or building blocks for both DNA and RNA are called _____ .

3. The name _____ is given to a set of genes which are linked together and which are transcribed as a unit.

4. The complementary strands in a DNA molecule are arranged in opposite directions and are said

   to be _____ .

5. The name _____ is given to a set of three nucleotides on mRNA that code for a particular amino

   acid. The name _____ is given to its complementary set of nucleotides on tRNA.

6. DNA replication is described as _____ because each new molecule contains one new DNA strand and one of the original DNA strands.

7. One strand of a DNA molecule is said to be _____ to the other strand.

8. RNA synthesis in which the genetic code is transferred from DNA to mRNA

   is called _____ .

9. The sequence of nucleotides in DNA serves as a _____ or pattern, which is copied into a complementary strand of either DNA or mRNA.

10. The _____ of a gene does not code for amino acids, but rather contains nucleotide sequences where molecules bind and control the expression of the gene.

11. The point at which nucleotides are added during DNA replication is called the

    replication _____ .

12. The two main methods by which biosynthetic pathways are controlled are _____ repression

    and _____ inhibition.

13. The metabolites that activate gene transcription are called _____ .

SELF-TEST OF READING MATERIAL

1. The best definition of a gene is
   a. a sequence of nucleotides in DNA that codes for a functional product.
   b. a segment of DNA.
   c. three nucleotides that code for an amino acid.
   d. a sequence of nucleotides in RNA that codes for a functional product.
   e. a segment of RNA.

2. Which of the following is a product of transcription?
    a. a new strand of DNA
    b. protein
    c. mRNA
    d. polypeptide
    e. All of the above are products of transcription.

3. If a segment of one strand of a DNA molecule had the nucleotide sequence AGTTACGGTAAT, what would the sequence on the complimentary strand be?
    a. UCAAUGCCAUUA
    b. ATTACCGTAACT
    c. TCAATGCCATTA
    d. TGCAATGGATCG
    e. AGTTACGGTAAT

4. Which of the following RNA's transports the amino acids to the ribosomes during protein synthesis?
    a. cRNA
    b. rRNA
    c. mRNA
    d. tRNA
    e. fRNA

5. In a DNA molecule, which of the following base pairing is normally observed?
    1. A-G
    2. C-G
    3. A-T
    4. A-U
    5. U-C
        a. 1,2
        b. 2,3
        c. 2,4
        d. 3,5
        e. 1,5

6. The backbone of the strands of a DNA molecule is made of alternating units of
    a. deoxyribose and purine.
    b. ribose and purine.
    c. deoxyribose and pyrimidine.
    d. ribose and phosphate.
    e. deoxyribose and phosphate.

7. The chemical composition of DNA includes which of the following?
    1. uracil
    2. ribose
    3. thymine
    4. deoxyribose
    5. one strand
    6. two strands

        a. 1,4,5
        b. 2,3,6
        c. 1,2,6
        d. 2,3,5
        e. 3,4,6

8. In prokaryotic cells transcription and translation both occur in the cytoplasm, while in eukaryotic cells transcription occurs in the nucleus and translation occurs in the cytoplasm.
    a. True
    b. False

9. Translation is also know as
    a. DNA synthesis.
    b. protein hydrolysis.
    c. reverse transcription.
    d. RNA replication.
    e. protein synthesis.

10. The site of protein synthesis in prokaryotic cells
    a. are the mitochondria.
    b. is the LPS.
    c. are the ribosomes.
    d. is the cell membrane.
    e. is the nucleoid.

11. The metabolites that activate gene transcription are called
    a. repressors.
    b. operators.
    c. inducers.
    d. synthesizers.
    e. promoters.

12. Feedback inhibition involves the inhibition of only the first enzyme of the biosynthetic pathway while end product repression prevents the synthesis of all of the enzymes of the pathway.
    a. True
    b. False

13. Anticodons are found on which of the following types of nucleic acids?
    a. DNA
    b. tRNA
    c. cDNA
    d. mRNA
    e. rRNA

14. Initiation, elongation, and termination are steps involved in which of the following processes?
    a. transcription
    b. translation
    c. replication
    d. a and b are both correct
    e. a and c are both correct

15. Enzymes not subject to regulation by induction or repression are called
    a. repressor enzymes.
    b. constitutive enzymes.
    c. penicillinase.
    d. promoter enzymes.
    e. inducible enzymes.

REVIEW QUESTIONS

1. Diagram the flow of information during DNA replication, and RNA and protein synthesis.

2. Compare the functions of the three types of RNA.

3. Distinguish between feedback inhibition and end product repression.

4. Complete the following table describing three major differences in transcription and translation in prokaryotes and eukaryotes.

PROKARYOTES	EUKARYOTES
1. Transcription and translation occur together	1.
2.	2. mRNA is processed before translation
3.	3. mRNA often transcribed as polygenic mRNA

7 *BACTERIAL GENETICS*

Bacterial genetics is probably the fastest growing area of microbiology today. Elucidation of the chemical structure of DNA has quickly led to an understanding of how cells function at a molecular level. This chapter describes the structure of DNA as well as how changes in that structure produces mutations. These mutations are spontaneous but can increase in frequency in the presence of mutagens. Bacteria are not considered sexually reproducing organisms, but there are processes by which some bacteria can undergo genetic recombination. These processes are used to better understand the genetics of bacteria.

KEY CONCEPTS

1. Antibiotics and other harmful agents in the environment do not cause mutations, but rather select for pre-existing mutations in the population.
2. In bacteria, small pieces of the chromosome can be transferred from one cell to another.
3. Genes can move from one location in DNA to other locations in the DNA of the same cell.
4. Plasmids confer a large number of different, but dispensable properties on bacteria, and are readily transferred to other bacteria, often unrelated to each other.
5. Bacteria are able to protect themselves from foreign DNA entering the cell.

SUMMARY

I. Source of Diversity in Microorganisms
    A. Two major sources account for diversity.
        1. Variation in sequences of nucleotides that exist in DNA.
        2. The environment regulates gene function and enzyme activity.

II. Alterations in Nucleotide Sequence in DNA
    A. Mutations can occur by substitution of one nucleotide for another.
    B. Mutations can occur by the removal or addition of nucleotides.
    C. Mutagens increase the frequency of mutations.

III. Mutagenesis Is the Process by Which a Mutation Is Produced
    A. Spontaneous mutations occur in the absence of any known mutagen. These mutations are, however, the same types as those caused by mutagens.
    B. Three types of mutagens are known. These are chemical agents, transposable elements, and radiation.
    C. Chemical mutagens often act by altering the hydrogen-bonding properties of the bases.
        1. Chemical mutagens include alkylating agents, base analogs, and intercalculating agents.
        2. Base analogs are incorporated into DNA in place of the natural base.
        3. Intercalating agents result in the addition of nucleotides.

IV. Transposable Elements
    A. Transposable elements are segments of DNA that move from one site in a DNA molecule to another. They insert into genes and disrupt their function.
    B. Insertion sequence is the simplest transposable element. It is composed of two inverted sequences flanking an enzyme required for transposition.
    C. More complex transposable elements code for antibiotic resistance.

V. Ultraviolet Irradiation—Ultraviolet Light and X Rays Are Mutagenic
    A. Ultraviolet light causes formation of thymine dimers.

VI. Repair of Damaged DNA
   A. UV damage can be overcome by an inducible enzyme system of DNA replication that bypasses the damaged DNA, but makes many mistakes. This is the SOS system.
   B. Visible light activates an enzyme that breaks covalent bonds, forming thymine dimers, the process called light repair.
   C. Bacteria can excise damaged DNA and replace it with undamaged DNA, which is called excision repair or dark repair.

VII. Rates of Mutation
   A. Genes mutate independently of one another and mutations are stable.
   B. Mutations are expressed rapidly in prokaryotic cells because they have only one or two identical chromosomes.

VIII. Mutant Selection
   A. Direct Selection requires that the mutant grow on a solid medium on which the parent cannot.
   B. Indirect selection must be used to isolate mutants that cannot grow on a medium on which the parent can grow.
      1. Replica plating involves transferring all of the colonies on one plate to another plate, simultaneously.
      2. Penicillin enrichment increases the proportion of mutants in a population. It is based on the fact that penicillin kills growing cells only.

IX. Conditional Lethal Mutants
   A. Conditional lethal mutants result from mutations in genes that would ordinarily be lethal.
   B. These conditional lethal mutations are usually in genes that are involved in macromolecular synthesis.

X. Chemicals can be tested for their cancer-causing ability by their mutagenic activity. The Ames test measures the frequency of reversion of his⁻ to his⁺ cells.

XI. Mechanism of Gene Transfer—General Aspects
   A. Genes can be transferred between bacteria by three different mechanisms.
   B. Only short segments of DNA are transferred.
   C. Recombination between donor and recipient DNA occurs by breakage and reunion mechanism.
      1. DNA-mediated transformation involves the transfer of naked DNA. Recipient cells must be able to take up DNA through their envelope—natural competence. Cells that can have holes punched in their envelopes with an electric current—artificial competence.
      2. Transduction involves viral transfer of DNA.
      3. Conjugation requires cell-to-cell contact. Usually only plasmids are transferred from F⁺ to F⁻ cells. Hfr cells are formed if the F⁺ plasmid integrates into the chromosome. Hfr cells can transfer chromosomal DNA. F' donor cells result when the F⁺ plasmid integrated into the chromosome is excised and carries a piece of chromosomal DNA with the plasmid.

XII. Plasmids
   A. R-factor plasmids confer resistance to a large number of antimicrobial agents. They can be transferred often to related and unrelated bacteria by conjugation.

XIII. Gene Transfer Within the Same Bacterium
   A. Transposable elements are important for the transfer of genes to unrelated bacteria because they can move from a chromosomal site to a plasmid, which can then be transferred by conjugation.

XIV. Restriction and Modification of DNA
   A. DNA entering unrelated bacteria is recognized as being foreign and is degraded by deoxyribonucleases termed restriction enzymes, which cleave the DNA at restricted or specific sites.
   B. Modification enzymes confer resistance to restriction by altering the nucleotides in the DNA, at the sites where the restriction enzymes cleave the DNA.

XV.   Importance of Gene Transfer to Bacteria
    A. Gene transfer allows microorganisms to survive changing environments by providing recipient cells with whole new sets of genes.

XVI. Importance of Gene Transfer to the Microbial Geneticist
    A. Gene mapping—Genes that are close together will be transferred together by conjugation, transformation, and transduction. Analysis of these transfers allows for the calculation of relative distances between genes.
    B. Genetic Engineering—Gene transfer is the method that genetic engineers use to introduce DNA into bacteria.

TERMS AND DEFINITIONS

1. The genetic constitution of an organism is its _____ while the characteristics displayed by an organism in a given environment comprise the _____ of the organism.

2. Bacteria are called _____ because they contain one or sometimes several identical chromosomes, but never pairs of chromosomes.

3. _____ protect bacterial cells from foreign DNA entering into them.

4. The deletion or addition of one or more nucleotides in a DNA molecule causes a misreading of the codons and is termed a _____ mutation.

5. _____ is a simple, inexpensive, and quick microbiological test for potential carcinogens.

6. The _____ is an appendage on a donor cell that attaches to a recipient cell during conjugation.

7. Compounds that resemble the chemical structure of nitrogen bases closely enough that they are incorporated into DNA and result in mutations are know as _____ .

8. Bacterial viruses are also called_____ .

9. Chemical or physical agents that increase the frequency of mutations are called_____ .

10. An _____ is a bacterium that requires a growth factor in order to grow, while a _____ does not require a growth factor.

11. A change in the nucleotide sequence of DNA that results in a recognizable change in the organism is called a _____ .

12. DNA that may exist either extrachromosomally or as part of the chromosome is termed an_____ .

13. _____ is the process by which a cell phenotype changes back to its original state through a mutation.

14. _____ are special segments of DNA that can move from one site in a DNA molecule to another. Another name for these special segments is _____ .

SELF-TEST OF READING MATERIAL

1. The genome of an organism includes genes from
   a. chromosomes.
   b. nucleotides.
   c. plasmids.
   d. a and b
   e. a and c

2. Genotypic changes are rare and usually involve only a few cells in a population while phenotypic changes will involve almost all of the cells in a population.
   a. True
   b. False

3. In the Ames test for mutagens, extract of rat liver is added to the test because
   a. it is a good source of nutrients.
   b. the extract can convert test compounds to active carcinogens.
   c. it contains mRNA necessary for the test.
   d. it neutralizes toxic materials in the test.
   e. it contains DNA necessary for the test.

4. Resistance to many antibiotics is carried on
   a. R factor plasmids.
   b. sex pili.
   c. enzymes.
   d. chromosomes.
   e. A factor plasmids.

5. Ultraviolet light is selectively absorbed in the cell by
   a. enzymes.
   b. DNA.
   c. cell membranes.
   d. proteins.
   e. RNA.

6. Which of the following chemical mutagens will result in the addition of nucleotides to the DNA?
   a. base analogs
   b. alkylating agents
   c. intercalating agents
   d. nitrous acid
   e. All of the above agents.

7. Mutations are expressed more frequently in bacteria because they
   a. divide often.
   b. are competent.
   c. divide infrequently.
   d. are diploid.
   e. are haploid.

8. The technique of replica plating involves transferring all of the colonies on one plate simultaneously to another plate.
   a. True
   b. False

9. The segments of DNA transferred between cells are
   a. large.
   b. single-stranded.
   c. small.
   d. circular.
   e. not functional.

10. Thymine dimer formation is the result of exposing DNA to
    a. ultraviolet light.
    b. base analogs.
    c. transposons.
    d. X-rays.
    e. intercalating agents.

11. The process of DNA repair in which enzymes cut out a damaged section of DNA and other enzymes then repair the resulting break is known as
    a. excision repair.
    b. SOS repair.
    c. photoreactivation.
    d. light repair.
    e. DNA cannot be repaired.

12. When bacteria develop resistance to an antibiotic, the antibiotic does not cause the mutation but only selects for a pre-existing mutation.
    a. True
    b. False

13. An organism which requires a growth factor in order to grow is called a(n)
    a. prototroph.
    b. wild type.
    c. autotroph.
    d. auxotroph.
    e. heterotroph.

14. The Ames test for chemical mutagens
    1. is less expensive than animal testing.
    2. uses the mutation of a his$^+$ cell.
    3. is faster than animal testing.
    4. is more expensive than animal testing.
    5. uses the reversion of a his$^-$ mutant.
    6. takes longer than animal testing.

    a. 1,2,3
    b. 1,3,5
    c. 1,2,6
    d. 4,5,6
    e. 2,4,6

15. Conjugation differs from transformation and transduction in that it requires contact between the donor and the recipient.
    a. True
    b. False

REVIEW QUESTIONS

1. Compare light and dark repair of DNA.

2. Distinguish between genotype and phenotype.

3. Describe three ways in which mutations may occur.

4. What is the relationship between mutagens and carcinogens.

5. List three advantages of the Ames test compared to animal testing.

ANSWERS:
  Terms and Definitions
    1. genotype/phenotype 2. haploid 3. restriction enzymes 4. frame shift 5. Ames test 6. sex pilus
    7. base analogs 8. bacteriophages 9. mutagens 10. auxotroph/prototroph 11. mutation 12. episome 13. reversion
    14. transposable elements/transposons
  Self-Test of Reading Material
    1. e 2. a 3. b 4. a 5. b 6. c 7. e 8. a 9. c 10. a 11. a 12. a 13. d 14. b 15. a

8 *MICROBIOLOGY AND BIOTECHNOLOGY*

Terms such as gene cloning, recombinant DNA, and genetic engineering are becoming commonplace in our language and our lives. Hardly a week goes by without one of these terms appearing in a news magazine or on the evening news broadcast. This chapter introduces you to the application of microbial genetics to areas of biotechnology. The methods of gene cloning, genetic engineering, and the polymerase chain reaction, which did not exist 20 years ago, are explored with examples of how these new technologies are important in today's society.

KEY CONCEPTS

1. DNA is a macromolecule that is easily studied and manipulated in a test tube.
2. The discovery of restriction enzymes opened the door to gene cloning and genetic engineering.
3. In the laboratory, DNA from one organism can be introduced to other organisms where it will replicate and be expressed.
4. Gene cloning can provide large amounts of specific DNA for study as well as large quantities of products coded by the cloned DNA.
5. The polymerase chain reaction technology is probably the most important technical advances made in molecular biology in the past decade.

SUMMARY

I. Recombinant DNA Technology Involves a Series of Techniques that Involve the Manipulation of a DNA Molecule Outside a Cell and Results in the Formation of New DNA Molecules. Two Techniques are of Special Importance.
   A. Gene cloning—propagating DNA of a particular cell in a new host cell.
   B. Genetic engineering—modifying the properties of cells by introducing recombinant DNA molecules that express their genes.

II. Basic Features of Genetic Engineering
   A. Techniques are fundamentally the same as natural processes occurring in cells to produce recombinant DNA molecules, but DNA may come from unrelated organisms.
   B. A common method of gene cloning involves the "shotgun" technique in which all of the genes of an organism are cloned and the gene of interest is then identified.
   C. The major steps in shotgun cloning are:
      1. Release of DNA from the host cell.
      2. Construction of recombinant DNA molecules. This involves restriction endonucleases and joining DNA to a plasmid.
      3. Introduction of recombinant DNA molecules into host organism (usually *E. coli*) by DNA transformation.
      4. Selection of host cells that contain recombinant DNA—usually by inoculating on antibiotic-containing medium.
      5. Identification of cells carrying the desired recombinant DNA clone usually done by hybridization to a known DNA probe.

III. Expression of Cloned Genes
   A. Gene expression requires that the host cell recognize the promoter, ribosome binding site, and stop signals for transcription and translation. These signals for expression can be cloned onto genes.
   B. The more closely related two organisms are, the more likely the genes of one will be expressed in the other.

IV. Application of Genetic Engineering in Biotechnology
   A. Microorganisms can be manipulated to give them new properties.
      1. Increasing the number of copies of a gene cloned on a multicopy number plasmid can increase the quantity of the protein coded by the gene.
   B. Clinically important proteins can be produced in *E. coli* and yeast. Such products include insulin, human growth hormone, blood clotting factors, interferons, and several different vaccines.

V. Additional Applications of Biotechnology
  A. Bioremediation involves the use of microorganisms to degrade harmful chemicals.
    1. Fertilizers have been applied to oil soaked beaches in Alaska to encourage the growth of existing microorganisms that then could break down the oil.
  B. Toxins from bacteria can serve as effective biocontrol agents for insects.
    1. The natural insecticides from *B. thuringiensis* (B. T. toxin) can be cloned into cells of *Pseudomonas,* which are killed and then applied to plants.
    2. The B. T. toxin gene can be cloned into a variety of plants, which then become resistant to insect pests.
  C. In plant genetic engineering, genes are introduced into the plants by *Agrobacterium.*
    1. To get bacterial genes expressed in plants, it is necessary to use a plant promoter and ribosome binding site as well as plant stop signals for gene expression.

VI. Biotechnology and the Polymerase Chain Reaction (PCR)
  A. Polymerase chain reaction allows researchers to duplicate specific pieces of DNA one billionfold in an hour.
  B. PCR involves the denaturation of DNA, annealing of two primers to either end of the DNA to be copied, and then synthesizing two strands from the primer, each complementary to one of the original strands. The cycle is then repeated.
  C. Microorganisms that cannot be cultured can still be identified using a combination of PCR technology, DNA sequencing, and probe technology.

TERMS AND DEFINITIONS

1. The gel used to separate DNA molecules is called _____ .

2. _____ is the analysis of DNA that is analogous to blood typing, which is becoming accepted for the identification of specific individuals in murder and rape cases.

3. _____ can be defined as DNA molecules that contain pieces of DNA not normally found together.

4. The production of cells with altered properties due to genes that have been inserted from other sources is known as _____ .

5. Substances found in human blood that have a variety of activities against viruses and that can be produced in genetically engineered cells is called _____ .

6. A fluorescent dye called _____ binds to nucleic acid molecules and is used to detect these molecules in gels.

7. _____ is a technique in which genes are removed from a cell and propagated in a new host cell where it multiplies.

8. The technique in which a radioactive probe is allowed to hybridize with a single-stranded DNA molecule to identify its complement is known as _____ .

9. _____ enzymes recognize and attach to specific base sequences in double-stranded DNA and break the bonds at these points.

10. A _____ is a molecule of either DNA or RNA which has the same nucleotide sequence as a gene you are trying to identify.

11. The entire set of cloned fragments from the genome of an organism is called _____ .

SELF-TEST OF READING MATERIAL

1. Which of the following organisms are used to introduce new genes into plants?
   - a. *E. coli*
   - b. *Agrobacterium*
   - c. His
   - d. *Salmonella*
   - e. *Bacillus*

2. The genes for insulin synthesis, which are cloned into *E. coli* came from
   - a. pigs.
   - b. *Salmonella.*
   - c. calf pancreas.
   - d. *E. coli.*
   - e. humans.

3. Which of the following processes does not result in recombination?
   - a. transformation
   - b. conjugation
   - c. transduction
   - d. replication
   - e. Two of the above are correct.

4. Which of the following can now be produced in microorganisms?
   1. insulin
   2. human growth hormone
   3. streptokinase
   4. blood clotting factors
   5. interferon
   - a. 1,2,4,5
   - b. 1,2,4
   - c. 1,2,5
   - d. 1,2
   - e. 1,2,3,4,5

5. One of the most widely used natural insecticides are the toxins produced by
   - a. *Bacillus thuringiensis.*
   - b. *Salmonella.*
   - c. *Bacillus stereothermophilis.*
   - d. *Bacillus cereus.*
   - e. *E. coli.*

6. Which of the following techniques allows an investigator to start with a single piece of DNA and produce billions of copies in a matter of hours?
   - a. transduction
   - b. gene cloning
   - c. polymerase chain reaction
   - d. recombinant technology
   - e. restriction analysis

7. Plasmids and viruses are the most common vectors used for gene cloning.
   - a. True
   - b. False

8. "Scissors" that are used to cut DNA into specific pieces at defined sites are the
   - a. repair enzymes.
   - b. SOS.
   - c. unrestricted endonucleases.
   - d. restriction endonucleases.
   - e. exonucleases.

9. A probe used to identify a gene can be
   - a. DNA.
   - b. a protein.
   - c. RNA.
   - d. a and b.
   - e. a and c.

10. Machines are now available that can synthesize nucleic acids of any sequence that an investigator might desire.
    - a. True
    - b. False

REVIEW QUESTIONS

1. Describe four advances in the last twenty years that have been instrumental in the development of biotechnology.

2. Outline the steps involved in gene cloning.

3. Describe a gene library.

4. What are two advantages of using natural insecticides such as the B. T. toxins instead of chemical insecticides.

5. Why is insulin produced by gene cloning better than that isolated from animal sources?

ANSWERS:
   Terms and Definitions
      1. agarose 2. DNA typing 3. recombinant DNA 4. genetic engineering 5. interferon 6. ethidium bromide
      7. gene cloning 8. Southern hybridization 9. restriction 10. probe 11. gene library
   Self-Test of Reading Material
      1. b 2. e 3. d 4. e 5. a 6. c 7. a 8. d 9. e 10. a

NOTES

9 CONTROL OF MICROBIAL GROWTH

The control of microbial growth is essential not only for health reasons but also for the preservation of the foods we eat, the clothes we wear, even the preservation of the homes where we live. Some methods of control, such as the preservation of food by drying or salting, are as old as civilization. Most methods of control are directed towards the most difficult forms of bacteria to kill, the endospores. A number of chemical or physical agents are available, but heat is probably the most common application. It is essential to understand the difference between an agent that is bacteriostatic and one that is bactericidal. Failure to understand this could have very serious consequences.

KEY CONCEPTS

1. Sterilization is the process of removing or killing microorganisms and viruses in or on a material. Disinfection, in contrast, implies only a reduction in the number of infectious agents to a point where they no longer present a hazard.
2. Time, temperature, growth stage of the organism, nature of the suspending medium and the numbers of organisms present must all be considered when determining which sterilization or disinfection technique to employ.
3. Sterilization and disinfection can be accomplished by using heat, filtration, chemicals, or radiation.
4. Death of infectious agents generally occurs logarithmically.

SUMMARY

I. Approaches to Control
   A. Sterilization is the process of killing or removing all microorganisms and viruses in or on a material.
   B. Disinfection reduces the number of pathogens but does not necessarily eliminate all living agents.

II. Principles Involved in Killing Microorganisms
   A. During sterilization, only a fraction of the microorganisms or viruses die during a given time interval.
   B. The time to achieve sterility depends partly on the number of organisms present at the beginning of sterilization.
   C. Different microorganisms and viruses vary in their susceptibility to sterilizing and disinfecting procedures.
   D. Numerous conditions alter the effectiveness of agents that kill microorganisms and viruses.

III. Killing Microorganisms and Viruses by Using Heat
   A. Heat kills by coagulating the proteins of cells and viruses.
   B. The use of heat is limited to substances that can withstand temperatures required for microbial killing.
   C. Dry heat requires more time than wet heat to kill microorganisms. Boiling kills vegetative cells and viruses but is not reliable for killing endospores.
   D. Pressure cookers and autoclaves are effective sterilizers if properly used.
   E. Pasteurization involves controlled heating at temperatures below boiling. It is not a sterilizing procedure, but eliminates many potential pathogens and delays spoilage.

IV. Sterilization by Filtration
   A. The effectiveness of filters depends on multiple factors such as pore size, chemical nature of the suspending fluid, and the amount of pressure to transfer fluid across the filter.
   B. Some membrane filters have such a small pore size that they are able to filter viruses from a suspension.

V. Chemical Disinfectants
   A. Chemical disinfectants are generally less effective in the presence of organic materials.
   B. Heat enhances their chemical action against microorganisms and viruses.
   C. Chemical disinfectants work slowly against bacterial endospores, *Mycobacterium tuberculosis* and certain small nonenveloped viruses.

    D. A disinfectant is chosen on the basis of its chemistry (phenolic, halogen, quaternary, etc.), the conditions under which it will be used (for example, a rubber material would not tolerate household bleach; quaternary ammonium compounds would be inactivated by pus or gauze), and how strict is the need for sterility.

    E. Alcohols are not effective against spores.

    F. Halogens include chlorine and iodine compounds. Iodophores release iodine, but are unreliable under certain conditions.

    G. Formaldehyde has limited use because it is slow to act against endospores and some viruses, the vapors are irritating, and it is a carcinogen.

    H. Phenolics include cresols and xylenols.

        1. In high concentrations most phenolics kill *Mycobacterium tuberculosis.*

        2. Some lack antiviral activity.

        3. Major advantages are wide spectrum of activity, reasonable cost, and ability of some to remain active in the presence soaps and other organic material.

        4. Hexachlorophene effectively prevents staphylococcal infections, but it has little activity against many Gram-negative bacteria, and absorption through the skin and through wounds is a potential hazard.

    I. Quaternary ammonium compounds are surface active substances that are effective sanitizing agents. Uses: disinfection of clean, inanimate objects, preservatives in non-food materials such as eye medicines. They have the disadvantage of being easily inactivated by soaps and other organic material including gauze.

    J. The use of metal compounds has decreased because of their generally bacteriostatic activity, inability to kill spores, and their contribution to serious pollution of natural water. Certain silver compounds continue to have important uses in preventing burn infections.

    K. Ethylene oxide should be handled with care because it is explosive and carcinogenic. It provides an effective alternative to heat sterilization.

  VI. Chemicals are commonly used as preservatives.

  VII. Radiation

    A. Gamma rays cause biological damage by producing hyperreactive ions. Ionizing radiation provides an alternative sterilizing method to ethylene oxide and heat, and has the advantages of not significantly altering the sterilized material and allowing immediate use of the object without airing.

    B. Ultraviolet radiation damages nucleic acids. It's use is limited to killing microorganisms in air and on clean surfaces.

TERMS AND DEFINITIONS

1. Gamma rays are an example of _____ radiation that causes biological damage by producing hyperreactive ions.

2. _____ is a term that indicates an antibacterial agent is primarily inhibits growth without substantial killing.

3. The complete killing or removal of all microorganisms and viruses from a material is called _____ .

4. Operating rooms and other patient care rooms are thoroughly cleaned and disinfected after use, a process known

   as _____ .

5. An _____ is a disinfectant that is compatible with human tissues.

6. According to public health standards, to _____ is to not only to substantially reduce the numbers of microorganisms on an object, but also to produce a product that has a clean appearance.

7. _____ is the process that reduces the number of potential pathogens on an object until they no longer represent a hazard.

8. An alcoholic solution of a substance is called a _____ .

9. The time required for 90% of the organisms in a population to be killed at a given temperature is called

   the _____ time.

10. The process of controlled heating of substances at temperatures below boiling which is directed toward the elimination

    specific pathogens is called _____ .

SELF-TEST OF READING MATERIAL

1. Which of the following would be the fastest way to kill endospores?
   a. autoclave at 121°C
   b. tincture of soap
   c. hot air oven at 180°C
   d. chlorox solution
   e. None of the above methods will kill endospores.

2. A substance used to disinfect human tissues is called a(n)
   a. antibiotic.
   b. disinfectant.
   c. antiseptic.
   d. sterilizer.
   e. germicide.

3. Which of the following causes the formation of thymine dimers in cellular DNA?
   a. X-rays
   b. base analogs
   c. gamma rays
   d. nitrous acid
   e. ultraviolet light

4. Which concentration of ethyl alcohol would is the most effective disinfectant?
   a. 100%
   b. 70%
   c. 60%
   d. 50%
   e. 30%

5. Which of the following best describes how cells in a population die when exposed to an antimicrobial agent?
   a. It depends on the species.
   b. The cells all die at once.
   c. It depends on the antimicrobial agent.
   d. The cells are never all killed.
   e. The cells in a population die exponentially.

6. Warmer temperatures generally interfere with the effectiveness of a disinfectant.
   a. True
   b. False

7. A chlorox solution and ethyl alcohol are examples of
   a. antiseptics.
   b. sterilizing agents.
   c. disinfectants.
   d. antibiotics.
   e. base analogs.

8. If a population of bacteria is exposed to steam at 121°C, the entire population will die at once because of the moist heat at this temperature.
   a. True
   b. False

9. A disinfectant is an antimicrobial agent which can be used on inanimate objects while an antiseptic is an antimicrobial agent which can be used on living tissue.
   a. True
   b. False

10. Tincture is a solution of
    a. iodine.
    b. chlorox.
    c. soap.
    d. alcohol.
    e. water.

11. Bacteriostatic substances will kill bacteria if allowed to remain in contact with them for long enough period of time.
    a. True
    b. False

12. Which of following is the least effective disinfectant?
    a. soap
    b. alcohol
    c. iodine
    d. cresol
    e. quats

13. Which of the following can be used for sterilizing materials?
    a. alcohol
    b. phenolic compounds
    c. ethylene oxide
    d. chlorine
    e. soap

14. Which of the following is most effective in killing bacteria?
    a. boiling at 100°C
    b. an autoclave at 121°C
    c. freezing and thawing several times
    d. freezing at -20°C
    e. a hot air oven at 180°C

REVIEW QUESTIONS

1. Distinguish between decontamination and disinfection.

2. Why can scrubbing prior to disinfection be helpful?

3. What are the most resistant and the least resistant types of microorganisms to chemical disinfectants?

4. During sterilization, if half of the bacteria present in a suspension are killed in the first minute, what fraction of those remaining are killed during the second minute? Does it matter what method of sterilization is being used?

5. If, in New Orleans, it takes 5 minutes to sterilize a suspension of bacterial cells by boiling, would you predict it would take more or less time to accomplish the same sterilization in Denver? Explain your answer.

ANSWERS:
  Terms and Definitions
    1. ionizing 2. bacteriostatic 3. sterilization 4. terminal cleaning 5. antiseptic 6. sanitize 7. disinfection
    8. tincture 9. decimal reduction 10. pasteurization
  Self-Test of Reading Material
    1. a 2. c 3. e 4. b 5. e 6. b 7. c 8. b 9. a 10. d 11. b 12. a 13. c 14. b

NOTES

10 CLASSIFICATION AND IDENTIFICATION OF BACTERIA

A system for the classification of microorganisms is essential so that microbiologists can keep things straight. A system of classification helps microbiologists organize the volumes of information on the great variety of microbes into a manageable, logical scheme. Ideally, such a classification system would also show evolutionary relationships among the microorganisms. That is, it would illustrate how one organism is related to another. The methods of biotechnology now hold the promise of reaching the goal of a natural system of classification. A patient, sick from an infectious disease, however, does not care particularly what species of bacteria they have—they are just interested in getting well. Their recovery often depends on the proper identification of the infectious agent.

KEY CONCEPTS

1. The best classification schemes group organisms that are related through evolution and separate those that are unrelated.
2. At the present time, the classification scheme for bacteria is based not on evolution but on convenience, consisting of readily determined characteristics such as shape and type of metabolism.
3. The most convenient method of determining the evolutionary relatedness between organisms is based on comparing the sequence of nucleotides in their DNA.
4. Unexpected relationships between various bacteria have been revealed by comparing their 16S ribosomal RNA sequences.
5. In clinical laboratories, identifying the genus and species of an organism is more important than understanding its evolutionary relationship to other organisms.

SUMMARY

I. Problems in Classifying Organisms
   A. The primary purpose of any classification scheme is to provide easy identification of an organism.
   B. The best classification schemes are based on evolutionary relatedness.
   C. Species is the basic taxonomic unit in bacteria; species differ from one another in several features, determined by genes.

II. Present Day Classification Schemes
   A. Descriptions of bacteria are contained in a reference text, *Bergey's Manual of Systematic Bacteriology*, which is published in four volumes.

III. Numerical Taxonomy
   A. This technique measures the relatedness between organisms by determining how many characteristics the organisms have in common.

IV. Molecular Approaches to Taxonomy
   A. A comparison of the DNA base composition of organisms indicates whether or not they may be related.
      1. If the GC content of two organisms differs by more than a few percent, they cannot be related.
      2. Having the same GC content does not necessarily mean that two organisms are related.
   B. A comparison of the sequence of bases in DNA can help determine the relatedness of organisms.
      1. Nucleic acid hybridization is the most widely used and accurate way to determine how organisms are related to one another.
   C. Amino acid sequence similarities in the same protein can indicate relatedness between organisms.
      1. Only a minute portion of the total genetic information of the cell is measured by this method.

      D. Determining the base sequence in 16S ribosomal RNA reveals evolutionary relationships between diverse groups of bacteria.
          1. This technique allows evolutionary relations to be seen between organisms that are not seen by nucleic acid hybridization.
          2. Certain sequences in 16S ribosomal RNA are always found in one of three groups of organisms and identify the organism as belonging to the eubacteria, archaebacteria, or eukaryotes.

  V. Methods of Identifying Bacteria
      A. The more tests that are run, the more accurate the identification.
      B. There are four major approaches: direct techniques, culture techniques, detection of microbial by-products, and molecular biological techniques.
      C. Direct methods of identification involve microscopic examination of specimens without culturing the organisms.
          1. Wet mounts are made.
          2. Stains, especially the Gram stain, are useful if enough organisms are present.
          3. Many harmful bacteria cannot be distinguished from non-harmful bacteria by their appearance.
      D. Culture techniques involve growing the organisms in pure culture.
          1. The specimen that is cultured depends on symptoms of disease.
          2. Culturing specimens may be necessary if infectious agents are present in small numbers.
          3. Isolated organisms can be precisely identified.
      E. Detecting products of metabolism may be easier and faster than culturing the organism.
          1. By-products can be measured by assaying for breakdown products of labeled energy sources.
          2. This technique allows faster identification of the organisms and therefore faster treatment.
      F. Molecular approaches in diagnostic microbiology usually involve analysis of DNA.
          1. Nucleic acid hybridization between the DNAs of two organisms—one known, the other unknown—will indicate whether or not they are related.
          2. Comparison of the cleavage pattern of two DNA samples—one from a known, another from an unknown organism—by the same restriction enzyme will indicate whether or not they are related.
          3. DNA probes can be used to identify species of bacteria in their natural environment or after culture.

  VI. Identifying Unculturable Organisms
      A. Microorganisms that cannot be cultured can still be identified.
          1. One technique is to copy by PCR a piece of DNA that is specific to one of the major cell kingdoms (eubacteria, archaebacteria or eukaryotes) and compare the sequence next to the signature sequences from previously identified organisms.
          2. PCR technology can be used to detect the presence of a single organism or virus particle in any environment.

TERMS AND DEFINITIONS

1. The technique for comparing the sequences of bases in DNA to determine the relatedness of organisms is

    termed_____ .

2. _____ is the arranging of organisms into related groups.

3. If two organisms differ only in minor phenotypic properties, then one organism may be considered a

    _____ rather than another species.

4. _____ is the science of classification.

5. The DNA base composition of an organism is usually expressed as the percent of guanine plus cytosine and is known as the _____ .

6. _____ microbiology is the area of microbiology concerned with the identification of infectious agents.

7. The _____ is the basic taxonomic unit for all organisms, but its definition is different for microorganisms compared to plants and animals.

8. An approach to taxonomy in which a large number of characteristics are compared and a percentage of common characteristics is calculated to show relatedness is called _____ taxonomy.

SELF-TEST OF READING MATERIAL

1. The GC content of two organisms was found to be 23% and 24%. Which of the following statements is true?
   a. The two organisms are closely related to each other.
   b. The two organisms are not closely related to each other.
   c. The two organisms are closely related only if they belong to the same taxonomic group.
   d. The similarity in GC contents may be coincidental and the organisms are not related.
   e. Two of the above are correct answers.

2. Bacteria are not given species names because they do not reproduce sexually and do not meet the definition of a species.
   a. True
   b. False

3. The ideal system of classification would be based on
   a. structure.
   b. easily observed characteristics.
   c. phenotypes.
   d. evolutionary relationships.
   e. PCR.

4. A surprising result of the analysis of 16S ribosomal RNA demonstrated that
   a. archaebacteria are a separate group from the prokaryotes.
   b. prokaryotes and eukaryotes actually belong to the same group.
   c. bacteria are closely related to certain plants.
   d. archaebacteria are a subgroup within and closely related to the prokaryotes.
   e. there are as many as a dozen different groups very distinct from each other.

5. Analysis of the sequence of amino acids in proteins gives _____ analysis of nucleotide sequences in DNA.
   a. considerably more information about the genetic composition of an organism than
   b. approximately the same information about the genetic composition of an organism as
   c. considerably less information about the genetic composition of an organism than

6. Direct examination for the identification of an infectious agent is more useful for many parasitic diseases than it is for bacterial diseases.
   a. True
   b. False

7. When identifying an unknown organism
    a. a few selected tests are usually preferred for an accurate identification.
    b. culturing the organism is necessary before an identification can be made.
    c. the more tests that can be made the better.
    d. only the techniques of molecular biology are accepted as valid.
    e. Two of the above answers are correct.

8. The Gram stain is not sensitive or specific enough to be of any practical use in the clinical laboratory.
    a. True
    b. False

REVIEW QUESTIONS

1. Based on a comparison of the 16S ribosomal RNA, what are the three distinct cell types?

2. Distinguish between an artificial system of classification and a natural system.

3. How is a species defined for bacteria compared to animals?

4. Why are DNA probes such powerful tools in classification and identification of bacteria?

ANSWERS:
    Terms and Definitions
        1. nucleic acid hybridization 2. classification 3. strain 4. taxonomy 5. GC content 6. diagnostic 7. species
        8. numerical
    Self-Test of Reading Material
        1. e 2. b 3. d 4. a 5. c 6. a 7. c 8. b

11 PROKARYOTIC MICROORGANISMS: EUBACTERIA AND ARCHAEBACTERIA

This chapter is a survey of the major groups of prokaryotic microorganisms as outlined in the *Bergey's Manual of Systematic Bacteriology.* In an introductory course, students of microbiology come to think of bacteria only in terms of the garden variety types such as *E. coli.* This would be like thinking of birds as all being sparrows. The diversity of bacteria is not only extreme, but also, even beautiful. Bacteria that kill other bacteria, bacteria with stalks, bacteria that look like fungi, and bacteria that live where we thought nothing could live are only a few examples of those introduced in this chapter.

KEY CONCEPTS

1. Prokaryotes show extreme diversity in appearance, growth requirements, and metabolism.
2. Some prokaryotes prey on other prokaryotes.
3. Some prokaryotes can multiply only as symbionts within eukaryotic cells.
4. Prokaryotes are vitally important in the recycling of carbon, nitrogen, and sulfur.
5. Although they have a prokaryotic cell structure, archaebacteria are probably more closely related to eukaryotes than to eubacteria.

SUMMARY

I. Prokaryotes that Have a Gram-negative Type of Cell Wall
   A. The spirochetes
      1. Spirochetes are flexible and have a spiral shape. Axial filaments contribute to their mobility.
   B. Aerobic, motile, helical or comma-shaped Gram-negative bacteria.
      1. This group of spiral and comma-shaped Gram-negative bacteria have a rigid cell wall, move by means of flagella, and require oxygen for growth.
      2. Microaerophiles require an atmosphere containing oxygen, but a much lower concentration than in air.
      3. *Bdellovibrios* prey on other Gram-negative bacteria, reproducing between the cell wall and cytoplasmic membrane.
   C. Gram-negative aerobic bacilli and cocci
      1. This large, diverse group of Gram-negative bacteria is characterized by rod or coccoid shape and aerobic growth requirement.
      2. *Rhizobium* species are important in converting atmospheric nitrogen, N_2, to a form usable by plants (nitrogen fixation). They live within the root cells of many plant species.
      3. Pseudomonads often produce non-photosynthetic pigments that can color the medium green in some cases. They utilize many complex organic compounds. Some can use nitrate (NO_3^-) ion as a substitute for molecular oxygen (O_2), an example of anaerobic respiration.
      4. Azotobacteria are soil organisms that can fix nitrogen under aerobic conditions.
   D. Facultatively anaerobic Gram-negative rods
      1. Facultatively anaerobic Gram-negative rods grow best aerobically but can also grow anaerobically if a suitable organic substrate is present.
      2. Enterobacteria include *Escherichia coli,* universally present in the human intestine.
      3. Vibrios and related bacteria are mostly marine organisms. Some possess luciferase and are luminescent.
   E. Anaerobic Gram-negative straight, curved and helical rods
      1. Anaerobic, Gram-negative, fermentative rods have various shapes and are inhibited or killed by oxygen. Some species inhabit the body cavities of humans.
   F. Dissimilatory sulfate- or sulfur-reducing bacteria
      1. Dissimilatory sulfate- or sulfur-reducing bacteria utilize sulfur or oxidized sulfur compounds as a final electron acceptor. They are important in recycling sulfur .

G. The rickettsias and chlamydias
1. Rickettsias and chlamydias are generally unable to grow outside the cells of a host animal. They are transmitted from one host to another by insects, mites, and ticks. Nucleic acid studies show rickettsias to be genetically unrelated to chlamydias.
2. Chlamydias multiply as a vegetative form and then differentiate into an infectious form. They are a unique group, lacking peptidoglycan in their cell walls.

H. Endosymbionts
1. Endosymbionts live within the cells of eukaryotic hosts in a stable association that can be beneficial to both organisms. Mitochondria and some chloroplasts of eukaryotes probably evolved from prokaryotic endosymbionts.
2. In endosymbionts of protozoa, environmental factors can upset the endosymbiotic relationship, leading, in some cases, to the death of both host and endosymbiont.
3. Many types of endosymbionts of other eukaryotes are known, including endosymbionts of insects and parasitic worms.

I. Gliding, non-photosynthetic bacteria
1. Gliding bacteria move slowly by an unknown mechanism when in contact with a surface. They can break down complex polysaccharides such as cellulose. One species causes a disease of fish.

J. Myxobacteria
1. The myxobacteria are gliding, fruiting bacteria. They can produce fruiting bodies, macroscopic aggregation of resting cells called microcysts, which are more resistant to heat, drying and radiation than the vegetative cells. Chemical signals are involved in initiating and coordinating the action of the individual cells.

K. Sheathed Bacteria
1. Sheathed bacteria are unbranching, filamentous forms in which the filament is enclosed in a sheath of lipoprotein-polysaccharide material. The sheath protects the bacteria and attaches them to solid structures. Sheathed bacteria may form brown scum in polluted streams, and they can plug pipes used in sewage treatment systems.

L. Anoxygenic photosynthetic bacteria
1. Anoxygenic phototrophs obtain their energy from sunlight, but do not produce oxygen as a by-product of photosynthesis. They require anaerobic growth conditions and a hydrogen donor other than water. Their ancestors probably predominated in the early history of the earth.

M. Oxygenic photosynthetic bacteria
1. Cyanobacteria are phototrophs that, like algae and plants, liberate oxygen during photosynthesis.
2. Their chlorophyll type and photosynthetic process are essentially the same as those of algae and plants, but unlike these eukaryotes, many species of cyanobacteria can fix nitrogen.
3. Accessory pigments called phycobiliproteins help trap light energy.

N. Budding and/or appendaged bacteria
1. Prosthecate and budding bacteria have projections of their cytoplasm into unusual structures. The structures function in attachment and increase area for absorbing nutrients.

O. Aerobic chemoautotrophic bacteria
1. The chemolithotrophic bacteria can grow in the dark using an inorganic substance as an energy source and CO_2 for a carbon source. There are four types: nitrifiers, sulfur oxidizers, hydrogen oxidizers, and metal oxidizers.

II. Prokaryotes that have a Gram-positive Type of Cell Wall
A. Gram-positive cocci
1. Gram-positive cocci may occur in a chainlike arrangement or in clusters. Aerobic, facultative, and anaerobic forms exist. One group is remarkably radiation resistant.

B. Regular non-spore-forming Gram-positive rods
1. The cylindrical non-spore-forming Gram-positive rods, compose a group of mostly unicellular organisms with smooth, straight outlines.
2. Genus *Lactobacillus*—some species help protect against infectious disease; others have essential roles in making pickles, yogurt, and other foods.

C. Irregular shaped, non-spore-forming, Gram-positive rods
1. Irregular, non-spore-forming Gram-positive rods may show misshapen cells, uneven or metachromatic staining, or branching chains of bacteria. Snapping division is common.

2. The corynebacteria are club-shaped and may show metachromatic staining. One species causes diphtheria.
3. Arthrobacters help degrade pesticides in soil. Their life cycle includes changes in shape, ranging from rod to coccus and back to rod.
4. Members of the genus *Actinomyces* grow as branching filaments that fragment into rods.

D. *Mycobacteria*
   1. *Mycobacteria* demonstrate the acid fast staining property. Unusual cell wall lipids make them resistant to staining by other methods and protect them against disinfectants.
   2. Certain species are responsible for tuberculosis and leprosy.

E. Actinomycetes with aerial and specialized hyphae
   1. Nocardioforms are filamentous organisms that usually form aerial mycelia and fragment into bacillary forms.
   2. Other Actinomycetes develop spores called conidia. Conidia are not as resistant as endospores, except in the genus *Thermoactinomyces*. Conidia occur in sacks, as in the genera *Frankia* and *Dermatophilus* genera. Streptomycetes and others include antibiotic-producing as well as disease-causing forms.

III. Prokaryotes that Lack Cell Walls
   A. The mycoplasmas
      1. The mycoplasmas lack cell walls. They appear to have evolved from an ancestor similar to Gram-positive bacteria. One group, the spiroplasmas, has species with a spiral shape and motility similar to spirochetes.

IV. Prokaryotes With Cell Walls that Lack Peptidoglycan
   A. Archaebacteria
      1. Archaebacteria are only distantly related to other prokaryotes. They lack peptidoglycan in their cell walls.
      2. They appear to have undergone less evolutionary change than eubacteria.
      3. They exist mainly today under conditions considered adverse for eubacteria.
      4. There are three kinds of archaebacteria: methanogens, halobacteria, and thermoacidophiles.

TERMS AND DEFINITIONS

1. Many species of eukaryotic organisms contain Gram-negative bacteria living inside their cytoplasm in a relationship known as _____ .

2. In _____ respiration, nitrate may be substituted for oxygen as the final electron acceptor.

3. _____ are flagella-like filaments that originate at the ends of a cell and overlap in the middle and are used for motility by spirochetes.

4. Three distinct groups of archaebacteria are the _____ , the _____ , and the _____ .

5. _____ are branching filaments found in actinomycetes and fungi.

6. On blood agar plates when red blood cells are completely destroyed leaving a clear area around the colony, the effect is called _____ .

7. In some organisms, the hyphal filaments are _____ meaning that the cytoplasm of each cell is continuous with that of adjacent cells because they do not have cell walls separating them.

SELF-TEST OF READING MATERIAL

Match the organisms on the left with their description on the right. A description may be used more than once and an organism may have more than one description.

_____ 1. *Neisseria gonorrhoeae*	a. spirochete
_____ 2. Archaebacteria	b. comma-shaped
_____ 3. *Mycoplasma*	c. bactivorus
_____ 4. Chlamydias	d. nitrogen-fixer
_____ 5. *Treponema pallidum*	e. sexually transmitted disease
_____ 6. *Bdellovibrio*	f. coccus
_____ 7. *Campylobacter jejuni*	g. obligate intracellular organism
_____ 8. *Vibrio cholerae*	h. salmon poisoning
_____ 9. *Rhizobium*	i. tuberculosis
_____10. *Neorickettsia*	j. walking pneumonia
_____11. *Mycobacterium*	k. growth in extreme environments
_____12. *Borrelia burgdorferi*	l. diarrhea and dysentery

REVIEW QUESTIONS

1. How do *Treponema pallidum, Borrelia burgdorferi,* and *Leptospira interrogans* differ in their transmission to human hosts?

2. What important function do some members of the genus *Rhizobium* perform for plants?

3. In what ways do rickettsias differ from chlamydias?

4. Explain the statement, " The genus *Pseudomonas* contains species with remarkably diverse biochemical capabilities."

5. How is the hypothesis for the endosymbiotic origin of mitochondria supported by the presence of endosymbiotes in *Paramecium*?

6. Give three examples of energy sources used by chemolithotrophs.

7. Distinguish among the three groups of archaebacteria.

8. What distinguishes mycoplasmas and spiroplasmas from other bacteria?

NOTES

ANSWERS:

Terms and Definitions

1. endosymbiosis 2. anaerobic 3. axial filaments 4. methanogens/halobacteria/thermoacidophiles 5. hyphae
6. ß-hemolysis 7. coenocytic

Self-Test of Reading Material

1. e,f 2. k 3. j 4. e,g 5. a,e 6. b,c 7. b,l 8. b,l 9. d 10. g,h 11. i 12. a

12 *EUKARYOTIC MICROORGANISMS: ALGAE, FUNGI, AND PROTOZOA*

The microbial world includes eukaryotic microorganisms as well as prokaryotic microorganisms and viruses. This chapter describes the three groups of eukaryotic microorganisms, the algae, fungi, and protozoa, with special emphasis on those that cause disease. The algae are not usually associated with disease except for certain types of poisoning due to toxins they produce. Members of the fungi can cause serious disease in plants and animals, including humans. Members of the protozoa are responsible for diseases such as malaria which affects the lives of millions of people.

KEY CONCEPTS

1. Algae, fungi, and protozoa are eukaryotic organisms and as such have eukaryotic cell structures. Many of these organisms are microscopic.
2. Algae are very important in the food chain and carbon cycle but are of minor importance in causing disease in humans.
3. Fungi play an important role in the decomposition of organic materials. They also cause a great deal of damage to food crops as well as other materials, and they are responsible for some serious diseases in humans.
4. Protozoa are single-celled often motile organisms that are an important part of zooplankton and the food chain. Some species cause disease that affect a large part of the world's population.

SUMMARY

I. Algae
   A. Algae are photosynthetic organisms that lack the complex tissue development of higher organisms.
   B. Algae are classified by photosynthetic pigments.
   C. Algae are found in a wide variety of habitats.
   D. Algae are typical eukaryotic organisms.
      1. Algal cell walls are rigid and contain cellulose.
      2. Microscopic algae are usually single cells but can also live as colonies.
      3. Macroscopic algae are multicellular with a variety of structures such as holdfasts, blades, bladders, and stipes.
      4. Reproduction in algae can be asexual or sexual. In some algae the generations alternate.
   E. Some dinoflagellates produce toxins that cause paralytic shellfish poisoning.

II. Fungi
   A. Fungi are non-motile, non-photosynthetic, heterotrophic organisms.
   B. Fungi are primarily terrestrial and occur in a large variety of habitats.
   C. The terms yeast, mold, and mushroom refer to morphological forms of fungi.
      1. Yeasts are single cells.
      2. Molds are filamentous.
      3. Mushrooms are the large fruiting bodies of certain fungi that are often edible.
      4. Dimorphic fungi exist as either yeast or mycelium, depending on conditions.
   D. Classification in fungi is frequently revised. In this text they are considered in three groups.
      1. Amastigomycota - terrestrial fungi
      2. Mastigomycota - water molds, flagellated lower fungi
      3. Gymnomycota - the slime molds
   E. Fungi cause disease in humans in four ways.
      1. Some people experience an allergic reaction to fungi.
      2. Ergot and aflatoxin are two fungal poisons that seriously affect humans.
      3. Fungal diseases are known as mycoses.
      4. Fungi destroy human food supply.

    F.   Fungi form symbiotic relationships with a variety of other organisms. Lichens and mycorrhizas are examples.

    G.   Fungi are economically important organisms.
1. They aid in the production of foods such as cheese, bread, beer, and wine.
2. They are a source of antimicrobial medicines.
3. They spoil foods and degrade organic materials.
4. They cause many plant diseases.
5. They are used for genetic and biochemical studies.
6. Genetically engineered yeasts produce many useful compounds such as insulin and growth hormone.

III.   Protozoa

    A.   Protozoa are microscopic, unicellular organisms that lack photosynthetic capabilities.

    B.   Protozoan habitats are diverse but they all require moisture in some form.

    C.   Classification of protozoa is based on their modes of locomotion.
1. Mastigophora-flagella
2. Sarcodina-pseudopodia
3. Sporozoa-flagella or nonmotile
4. Ciliata-cilia

    D.   Protozoa lack a cell wall but maintain their distinctive shape by other means.

    E.   Protozoa display polymorphism by taking on different forms in different environments.

    F.   Many protozoa take in nutrients by pinocytosis and/ or phagocytosis

    G.   Reproduction is by both asexual and sexual methods.

    H.   Protozoa are important as part of the food chain.

    I.   Protozoa cause a variety of serious diseases in humans.

TERMS AND DEFINITIONS

_____1.   Another name for fungal diseases.

_____2.   Free-floating, photosynthetic organisms in aquatic environments.

_____3.   Engulfment of large food particles.

_____4.   Vegetative or feeding form of a protozoan.

_____5.   The product of the fusion of two gametes.

_____6.   Reproduction by multiple fissions.

_____7.   Poison produced by fungi that may have been responsible for the Salem witch hunts.

_____8.   A mass of hyphae.

_____9.   A structure that anchors certain algae to a solid surface.

_____10.   A form of asexual reproduction in filamentous algae in which a portion breaks off to form a new organism.

_____11.   The uptake of soluble substances through a cell membrane.

a. phytoplankton
b. schizogony
c. holdfast
d. phagocytosis
e. fragmentation
f. pinocytosis
g. zygote
h. cyst
i. hypha
j. trophozoite
k. mycelium
l. lichens
m. rhizoids
n. ergot
o. mycoses

_____12. A single filament of a mold.

_____13. The result of the association of an alga and a fungus.

_____14. Specialized hyphae that anchor fungi to a substrate.

_____15. A resting form of a protozoan.

SELF-TEST OF READING MATERIAL

1. Which of the following is the most likely way to get an infection of *Giardia lamblia*?
   - a. mosquito bite
   - b. injection
   - c. ingestion of a cyst
   - d. inhalation of an endospore
   - e. ingestion of a trophozoite

2. Malaria is caused by which of the following organisms?
   - a. *Toxoplasma*
   - b. *Trypanosoma*
   - c. *Trichomonas*
   - d. *Giardia*
   - e. *Plasmodium*

3. Malaria is transmitted to humans by
   - a. ingesting cysts in water or food.
   - b. inhaling trophozoites.
   - c. mosquito bites.
   - d. dirty fingers.
   - e. handling cats.

4. A unique feature of the Sporozoans is that they
   - a. divide by transverse binary fission.
   - b. reproduce exclusively by sexual means.
   - c. are not motile in the adult form.
   - d. reproduce exclusively by asexual means.
   - e. have two types of nuclei.

5. Which of the following genera causes vaginitis?
   - a. *Toxoplasma*
   - b. *Giardia*
   - c. *Plasmodium*
   - d. *Trichomonas*
   - e. *Trypanosoma*

6. Which of the following statements describe protozoans?
   - a. They are eukaryotes.
   - b. They can be grouped on the basis of their means of motility.
   - c. They reproduce only by asexual means.
   - d. All of the above are correct statements.
   - e. Only a and b are correct.

7. Which of the following statements about the Deuteromycetes are true?
   - a. Their usual habitat is aquatic.
   - b. Sexual reproduction is absent or unknown.
   - c. Their cell walls are cellulose.
   - d. All of the above statements are correct.
   - e. a and b are correct statements.

8. Which of the following statements describe fungi?
   - a. They are eukaryotes.
   - b. Most fungi are anaerobic.
   - c. They reproduce only by sexual means.
   - d. All of the above statements are correct.
   - e. a and b are correct statements.

9. Fungal infections of the skin are called
   a. systemic mycoses.
   b. superficial psychoses.
   c. intermediate mycoses.
   d. superficial mycoses.
   e. yeasts.

10. Which of the following statements describe algae?
   a. They are eukaryotes.
   b. They may be either microscopic or macroscopic.
   c. They are classified according to their photosynthetic pigments.
   d. All of the above statements are correct.
   e. a and b are correct statements.

REVIEW QUESTIONS

1. Compare the algae, fungi, and protozoa . What characteristics do all these organisms have in common? What features of each cause them to be separated into distinct classification groups?

2. What characteristics of algae account for their general lack of disease-causing properties?

3. What properties of fungi account for their ability to be so destructive?

4. Although we think most often of protozoa as disease-causing organisms, what would the world be like if there were no protozoa?

NOTES

NOTES

13 *THE NATURE AND STUDY OF VIRUSES*

Viruses are very different from any of the cellular organisms that we have described for you. Their organization is at the macromolecular level, several steps below the organization of a cell, eukaryotic or prokaryotic. Viruses are little more than a few genes carried in a protein coat. They have no metabolic machinery of their own, and therefore, must rely upon that of their host cell. Viruses cannot replicate or reproduce outside of a host cell. Viruses infect both eukaryotic and prokaryotic cells. Much of our knowledge of viral replication is from studies of viral infections of bacteria. Viruses can confer new properties on their host cells.

KEY CONCEPTS

1. Viruses are a set of genes contained in a protein coat.
2. In order to multiply, viruses depend to varying degrees on the enzymatic activity of the cells they invade.
3. Viruses that infect bacteria serve as excellent models for viruses infecting animal and plant cells.
4. Viruses can replicate within cells which they lyse or they can become integrated into host cell DNA and confer new properties on the cells.
5. Different viruses can infect and replicate within all kinds of cells, both prokaryotic and eukaryotic.

SUMMARY

I. Viruses—General Characteristics
    A. Viruses have several features which distinguish them from cells.
        1. They are very small—100 to 1,000 times smaller in diameter than the cells they invade.
        2. They contain very few genes.
        3. The nucleic acids can be either DNA or RNA, but never both.
        4. Viral proteins and nucleic acids replicate separately.

II. Virus Architecture
    A. Viruses can have different shapes. Some are polyhedral (having many flat surfaces); others are helical and others are a combination of both.
    B. The shape of the virus is determined by the shape of its protein coat (capsid).
    C. Some viruses have only a capsid whereas some animal viruses have a lipid membrane (envelopes) surrounding the capsid.

III. Virus-Host Relationships Exemplified by Phage-Bacterial Interactions
    A. Three major types of relationships are known.
        1. Productive response in which more copies of virus are made and are released following lysis of the host cell.
        2. Productive response in which the virus leaves the cell without lysing it.
        3. Latent state in which the viral nucleic acid becomes integrated into the host chromosome.

IV. Virus Replication in a Productive Infection Resulting in Cell Lysis
    A. Step 1—Phages attach to specific sites on host bacteria.
    B. Step 2—Viral nucleic acid enters the host cell; protein coat remains on the outside.
    C. Step 3—Phage DNA is transcribed sequentially leading to production of specific proteins.
    D. Step 4—Phage DNA is replicated and phage structural proteins are synthesized independently.
    E. Step 5—Phage DNA and protein assemble to form mature virions—the maturation process.
    F. Step 6—Virions are released from the host cell by lysis of bacterial cell wall.

V. Phage Growth—A One-step Growth Curve
   A. This procedure involves assaying the number of virions inside and outside the bacteria at various times after adsorption.
   B. Samples are removed at various times, one set is treated with chloroform, the other is not. Samples are inoculated onto a lawn of bacteria to lyse them, leading to plaque, which represents the site at which a single phage or infected bacterial cell has landed.

VI. Viral Replication in a Latent State
   A. The DNA of temperate viruses is integrated into the host chromosome.
   B. Integration of phage DNA into the bacterial chromosome occurs because of identical DNA sequences in the phage and the bacteria.
   C. Repressor must function continuously to keep prophage in the integrated state.
   D. Activation of SOS repair systems destroys the repressor; the phage DNA is excised and virions are produced which lyse the cells.
   E. Lysogens are immune to infection by the same phage.
   F. Prophage often codes for proteins which alter the properties of the host (lysogenic conversion).
   G. Virus Can be Released Without Host Cell Lysis
      1. Viruses, such as filamentous phages, are released without killing the host cell. They leave the cell by extrusion.
      2. The virus is assembled as it leaves the host cell.

VII. Transduction
   A. Both virulent and temperate phages can transfer DNA of one host to another host.
      1. In generalized transduction, virulent phages can transfer any part of the genome.
      2. In specialized transduction, temperate phages can transfer only a specific set of genes.

VIII. Host Range of Viruses
   A. Any given virus can generally infect cells of only one or a few species.
   B. Limitation in host range is due to the fact that animal and bacterial viruses must adsorb to specific receptors on the host cell surface.

IX. Methods Used to Study Viruses
   A. Many eukaryotic host cells can be cultivated in the laboratory the technique of tissue culture.
   B. Cells from a normal vertebrate animal grow as a monolayer attached to the surface of a flask—but for only a limited number of generations before they die.
   C. Viruses can infect, multiply, and lyse cells growing in a monolayer, resulting in a readily observable clearing (plaques).
   D. Infected tissue culture cells undergo characteristic changes in their appearance depending on the virus.
   E. Quantal assays measures the number of infective virions by their effect on different host cell systems.
   F. The presence of some viruses can be detected because they can cause red blood cells to clump.

TERMS AND DEFINITIONS

_____ 1. Phages that can either replicate or integrate into the host chromosome

_____ 2. Viruses that have a lipid membrane acquired during release from the host cell

_____ 3. Viruses that infect bacteria

_____ 4. Changes in the appearence of virus-infected tissue culture cells

_____ 5. Process by which any gene can be transferred by a phage from one bacterium to another

_____ 6. Identical protein subunits composing the capsid of a virus

_____ 7. An area of clearing on a bacterial lawn indicative of a phage infection

_____ 8. The technique of cultivating animal cells in the laboratory

_____ 9. A bacterial cell carrying a prophage

_____ 10. Protective coat surrounding a virus nucleic acid core

_____ 11. An enzyme located in the tail of some phages that digests a small hole in the bacterial cell wall

_____ 12. A complete and infective virus particle

_____ 13. Genetic elements that can replicate as part of the chromosome or independently of it

_____ 14. Phage DNA integrated into the host cell DNA

_____ 15. Proteinaceous infectious agents

a. bacteriophages
b. virion
c. capsid
d. capsomeres
e. enveloped viruses
f. prion
g. lysozyme
h. plaque
i. temperate phage
j. prophage
k. lysogen
l. generalized transduction
m. episomes
n. tissue culture
o. cytopathic effect

SELF-TEST OF READING MATERIAL

1. A bacteriophage after it becomes integrated into its host's chromosome is called a(n)
   a. prophage.
   b. temperate phage.
   c. lysogen.
   d. intemperate phage.
   e. lytic.

2. List the following stages of the lytic cycle of bacteriophages in the proper sequence.
   1. phage DNA synthesized
   2. lysis
   3. penetration
   4. attachment
   5. phage DNA transcribed
   6. assembly

   a. 3,5,1,2,4,6
   b. 4,5,1,6,2
   c. 5,6,2,4,3,1
   d. 4,5,3,1,6,2
   e. 4,3,5,1,6,2

3. A complete infective virus particle is called a
   a. bacteriophage.   d. lysogen.
   b. viroid.   e. virion.
   c. prophage.

4. All viruses, except the bacteriophages, are obligate intracellular parasites.
   a. True
   b. False

5. In viruses that have envelopes, the origin of these envelopes is
   a. viral.   d. phage.
   b. host.   e. partially viral and partially host.
   c. bacterial.

6. A virion is a
   a. naked, infectious piece of RNA.   d. nucleic acid without a capsid.
   b. complete, infectious virus particle. e. a naked, infectious piece of DNA.
   c. capsid without a nucleic acid.

7. All viruses require a host cell for replication.
   a. True
   b. False

8. The transfer of genetic information, which is mediated by a bacteriophage, is called
   a. translation.   d. transformation.
   b. transduction.   e. transcription.
   c. transfusion.

9. Viruses, except for bacteriophages, contain a single type of nucleic acid.
   a. True
   b. False

10. Recent breakthroughs in techniques have resulted in the cultivation of viruses in cell-free medium in the lab.
    a. True
    b. False

REVIEW QUESTIONS

1. Describe four features that distinguish viruses from cells.

2. Viruses have a limited number of shapes. Why is this?

3. What is lysogenic conversion? Give an example.

4. Compare and contrast the types of transduction.

ANSWERS:
  Terms and Definitions
    1. i 2. e 3. a 4. o 5. l 6. d 7. h 8. n 9. k 10. c 11. g 12. b 13. m 14. j 15. f
  Self-Test of Reading Material
    1. a 2. e 3. e 4. b 5. e 6. b 7. a 8. b 9. b 10. b

NOTES

14 VIRUSES OF ANIMALS AND PLANTS

Although much of the biology of bacteriophages applies to animal and plant viruses, there are significant differences in viral infections of eukaryotic cells. This chapter explores some of those differences with an emphasis on animal viruses. You will be introduced to the classification of viruses and then a description of animal virus replication. Animal and plant viruses cause damage to their host cells in a variety of ways including tumor formation. The human immunodeficiency virus (HIV) is the causative agent of AIDS or the acquired immunodeficiency syndrome.

KEY CONCEPTS

1. Viruses are classified on the basis of their morphology, size, and the physical and chemical nature of their nucleic acid.
2. The interactions of animal viruses with their hosts are similar to the interactions between bacteriophages and bacteria.
3. The replication of viral nucleic acid depends to varying degrees on the enzymes of nucleic acid replication of the host cell.
4. Symptoms of viral-caused disease result from tissue damage of the host.
5. Some tumors in animals result from viral DNA becoming integrated into the host genome and coding for the synthesis of abnormal proteins, which interfere with normal control of host cell growth.

SUMMARY

I. Classification Scheme of Animal Viruses
   A. Animal viruses are classified into families, genera, and species based mainly on four characteristics:
      1. Size
      2. Nature of nucleic acid they contain
      3. Presence or absence of an envelope
      4. Shape of virus particle

II. Virus Interactions with Animal Cells
   A. Three kinds of viral-host cell interactions can be identified:
      1. productive infection which results in cell lysis
      2. persistent infections in which the virus often buds from the cell without killing it and
      3. latent infections in which viral nucleic acid is integrated into the host cell genome.

III. Virus Multiplication
   A. The first step in infection is adsorption of the virus to the host cell.
      1. Attachment proteins of the virus bind to specific host cell receptors.
      2. The host cell is resistant if it lacks receptors to the virus.
   B. Viral entry often involves fusion of the cytoplasmic membrane of the host with the virion envelope
      1. Naked virions enter by endocytosis.
   C. The replication of viral nucleic acid depends to varying degrees on enzymes of the host cell.
      1. Larger viruses generally encode more enzymes and are less dependent on host cell enzymes.
   D. Maturation of virions involves self-assembly of viral component parts.
   E. Virions are released as a result of lysis of dead cells or by budding from living cells.
      1. Animal and plant viruses do not use lysozyme.

IV. Interactions of Animal Viruses with Their Hosts
   A. In the case of animals, outcome of infection depends on many factors independent of the infected cell. These include defense mechanisms of the host.
   B. In most cases, viruses cause no obvious harm or disease.
   C. Most healthy humans carry a number of different viruses.
   D. Acute infections result in readily observed disease symptoms that disappear quickly.

    E.   In persistent infections the virus is present for many years without symptoms of disease.
        1.   Chronic infections are the same as persistent infections.
        2.   Slow viral diseases are a subgroup of persistent infections in which the disease progresses slowly and involves the central nervous system.
    F.   Latent viral infections may result from integration of viral DNA into host cell DNA.

V.   Viruses and Tumors in Animals
    A.   Tumors caused by DNA viruses result from integration and expression of viral DNA in the host cell.
    B.   Tumors caused by RNA viruses involve the making of a DNA copy of the viral RNA which is then integrated into the chromosome of the host cell.

VI.   Mechanisms of Cell Transformation by Viruses
    A.   The integrated viral DNA disrupts control of normal cell growth and tissue development.
    B.   Retroviruses integrate oncogenes which are similar to normal host genes termed protooncogenes. Oncogene gene products probably disrupt the function of protooncogene gene products.

VII.   Viruses and Tumors in Humans
    A.   Three groups of DNA viruses have been shown to cause tumors in humans. These are the Epstein-Barr virus, hepatitis B virus and the human papillomavirus.
    B.   There are other possible cancer-causing viruses. These include polyoma virus and adenovirus.
    C.   A rare human leukemia is caused by a retrovirus.
        1.   Human T-cell lymphotropic virus causes a rare cancer of a specific white blood cell—the T-cell.

VIII.   HIV Disease (AIDS)
    A.   HIV disease is caused by an RNA virus of the retrovirus family.

IX.   Viruses that Cause Disease of Plants
    A.   A large number of serious plant diseases are caused by viruses.
    B.   Plant viruses are spread by a variety of mechanisms.
        1.   Plant viruses are very resistant to inactivation.
        2.   Insects are most important for transfer.

X.   Insect Viruses
    A.   Some viruses can multiply in plants and insects.
    B.   Some viruses are highly pathogenic for insects and are used in biological control of insects.

XI.   Viroids
    A.   Viroids, short single-stranded RNA molecules, cause a variety of plant disease.

TERMS AND DEFINITIONS

_____ 1.	Transforming genes of retroviruses that are integrated into the host chromosome	a. spikes
		b. endocytosis
		c. budding
_____ 2.	RNA viruses that make a DNA copy and incorporate it into the host cell genome	d. carriers
		e. acute infections
		f. retrovirus
_____ 3.	Protein surface projections from viruses that are used for attachment	g. latent infections
		h. tumor
		i. transformed cells
_____ 4.	A mechanism for releasing enveloped virions from a host cell	j. provirus
		k. oncogenes
		l. viroid
_____ 5.	A term for a retrovirus after it has integrated into the host chromosome	

_____ 6. Diseases of relatively short duration

_____ 7. A naked, small, single-stranded infectious
RNA molecule

_____ 8. A method of viral penetration into animal cells

_____ 9. A hidden infection generally without symptoms

_____ 10. Individuals that harbor a virus and are infectious,
but do not have a disease

_____ 11. A swelling that results from the abnormal growth
of cells

_____ 12. Cells that have lost the ability to control their
growth

SELF-TEST OF READING MATERIAL

1. Animal viruses usually penetrate a host cell by
   a. injection.
   b. exocytosis.
   c. pili.
   d. endocytosis.
   e. a vector.

2. An envelope is acquired during which of the following steps?
   a. penetration
   b. lysis
   c. synthesis
   d. release
   e. assembly

3. When an animal virus becomes integrated into the host's chromosome it is then called a
   a. prophage.
   b. provirus.
   c. vegetative virus.
   d. temperate virus.
   e. temperate phage.

4. Which of the following statements about spikes on viruses is true?
   a. They contain lysozyme for rupturing the host cell.
   b. They function in recognition and attachment to host cells.
   c. They are proteins.
   d. b and c are correct.
   e. a and b are correct.

5. An RNA virus with reverse transcriptase will first synthesize a
   a. mRNA molecule.
   b. complementary strand of DNA.
   c. cDNA molecule.
   d. complementary strand of RNA.
   e. rRNA molecule.

6. An example of a chronic virus infection is
   a. cancer.
   b. hepatitis.
   c. chicken pox.
   d. herpes.
   e. Two of the above are correct.

7. Virtually all slow viral infections involve
   a. the central nervous system.
   b. a viroid.
   c. retroviruses.
   d. plasmids.
   e. digestive system.

8. An example of a latent virus infection is
   a. cancer.
   b. hepatitis.
   c. SSPE
   d. herpes.
   e. Two of the above are correct.

REVIEW QUESTIONS

1. Distinguish between chronic viral infections and latent viral infections. Give examples of each.

2. Describe three mechanisms by which animal viruses enter the host cell.

3. Complete the following table.

NORMAL CELLS	CANCER (TRANSFORMED) CELLS
1. Cells grow as a monolayer.	1.
2. Cells attach to each other and glass surface.	2.
3.	3. Cells grow indefinitely.
4. Cells do not form tumors.	4.

4. Describe the four characteristics used to classify animal viruses.

ANSWERS:
  Terms and Definitions
    1. k 2. f 3. a 4. c 5. j 6. e 7. 1 8. b 9. g 10. d 11. h 12. i
  Self-Test of Reading Material
    1. d 2. d 3. b 4. d 5. b 6. b 7. a 8. d

NOTES

15 INTERACTIONS BETWEEN HUMANS AND MICROORGANISMS

When a microorganism infects a human host, the outcome of that infection will depend on a dynamic interaction between the microorganism and the host. When the host defenses adequately protect the host, the infection is resolved, but when the infecting microorganism gets the upper hand, disease occurs. Good health, free of infection, is the result of this dynamic balance and depends on several factors. These include the person's defenses to resist infection and disease and the factors of the microorganism that help it overcome host defenses. This chapter explores the non-specific defense mechanisms of people and the virulence factors that microbes use to counter these defense mechanisms.

KEY CONCEPTS

1. The resident normal flora protects humans from invasion by pathogenic microorganisms but is also a potential source of pathogens.
2. A microorganism's ability to establish an infection depends upon a variety of factors including (1) the ability of the microorganism to attach to a host tissue, (2) the ability of the microorganism to invade host tissues, (3) the possession of toxins and (4) the state of the host defenses.
3. The host resists infection by both specific and nonspecific defense mechanisms.

SUMMARY

I. The host defends itself against invaders in two ways.
    A. Nonspecific mechanisms include physical barriers as well as physiological mechanisms.
    B. Specific immune response includes specialized cells and proteins that show an enhanced response to repeat infections.

II. Normal Flora of the Human Body
    A. Normal microbial flora constitute those organisms that colonize the host but do not normally produce disease.
    B. Microorganisms and humans form a variety of symbiotic relationships.
        1. Commensalism is an association in which one partner benefits but the other remains unaffected.
        2. Mutualism refers to an association in which both partners benefit.
        3. Parasitism refers to an association in which one organism benefits at the expense of the other organism.
    C. Normal flora is acquired from contacts with the environment.
    D. Normal flora is important to the health of the host.
        1. Normal flora includes potentially harmful organisms.
        2. Normal flora competes for nutrients and thus may exclude harmful organisms.
        3. Normal flora stimulates the immune system.
    E. The human-microorganism ecosystem is continually undergoing changes as a result of external factors including food, antibiotics, and moisture.

III. Mechanisms of Pathogenesis
    A. Infectious microorganisms can come from a variety of sources including other humans, soil, air, and water.
    B. Attachment is usually a necessary step in the establishment of an infection.
        1. Attachment by a microorganism does not necessarily imply infection, but is often a necessary prerequisite.
        2. The ligands of the microorganism fit in a lock-key arrangement with a receptor on the cell surface.
        3. Different microbial strains have different ligands; different cells have different receptors.

C. The establishment of infection usually involves the invasion of host tissues.
    1. Some epithelial cells ingest microorganism by a process resembling phagocytosis.
    2. Large concentrations of microorganisms may permit tissue invasion of the host tissues.
D. Colonization is a necessary step to establishing an infection.
E. Some pathogens can evade or thwart the work of the phagocytes.
    1. Phagocytosis involves attracting the phagocyte to the microorganism, engulfing it and killing it.
    2. Some phagocytes can avoid phagocytosis because they have a large capsule that prevents engulfment.
    3. Some microorganisms can remain alive and even multiply within the phagocytes.
F. Extracellular products enhance microorganisms ability to cause disease.
    1. Exotoxins are highly toxic, distinctive proteins released by certain species of microorganisms. They are destroyed by heating.
    2. Endotoxins are lipopolysaccharides from the cell walls of Gram-negative bacteria, which play a contributing role in infectious disease. They are not destroyed by heating.
    3. Other bacterial products such as phospholipase, hemolysin, coagulase, and others play a contributing role in infectious disease.
    4. Nonbacterial toxins include the neurotoxin produced by *Gonyaulax*, an alga, and aflatoxin produced by a fungus.

V. Host Factors Influencing Resistance to Infection
A. Circulating and tissue leukocytes are vital to the host defenses.
    1. The granulocytes include the polymorphonuclear neutrophils, eosinophils, and basophils.
    2. The mononuclear phagocytes and PMN are the major phagocytic cells in the body.
B. The principal events of inflammation include the following.
    1. Tissue injury followed by the release of chemical mediators.
    2. Blood vessel dilation and the increased flow of plasma together with redness, pain, and heat.
    3. White blood cell migration to area of injury.
C. Various non-specific antimicrobial and antiviral substances are present in body fluids including lysozyme, beta-lysin, interferons, and complement.
D. The host's metabolic response mobilizes the body to fight infection.
    1. Fever aids in the control of infection by having an adverse effect on the growth of the microorganism and enhances microbial defense reactions.
    2. Iron is removed from the circulation by phagocytic cells making it difficult for microorganisms to grow.
E. Impaired body defenses promote infectious disease.
F. Genetic factors, age, and stress are important in determining the susceptibility of people to certain infections.
G. Some pathogens live in host tissues for years held in check by host defenses.

TERMS AND DEFINITIONS

1. Host surface cell components that bind specifically to the surface of microorganisms are known

   as _____ .

2. _____ describes interactions that occur between different organisms that live in close association with each other on a more or less permanent basis.

3. The condition in which there is a noticeable impairment of body function is called _____ .

4. _____ is a protein carried to the hypothalamus by the bloodstream where the hypothalamus responds by increasing the body temperature.

5. The microorganisms that grow on the external and internal surfaces of the body without producing obvious harmful

   effects to these tissues are known as the _____ .

6. _____ are members of the normal flora that are able to cause disease under special circumstances.

7. Properties of microorganisms that enhance their disease-producing capabilities contribute to their_____ .

8. _____ occurs when a microorganisms penetrates the body surfaces, enters the body tissue, multiplies, and causes the host to interact with an immune or other type of response.

9. Microorganisms that inhabit the body only occasionally are termed_____ .

10. _____ is the lipid component of endotoxins that is responsible for the toxic properties of the endotoxin.

11. Projections from the surface of microorganisms or viruses that bind specifically to host cells.

    are called_____ .

12. _____ consists of a group of interacting serum proteins which provides a non-specific defense mechanism.

13. Vacuoles within macrophages that contain a variety of digestive enzymes are called _____

14. A _____ is any disease-producing microorganism.

SELF-TEST OF READING MATERIAL

1. Which of the following may contribute to a pathogen's virulence?
   1. endotoxins
   2. capsules
   3. ligands
   4. collagenase
   5. exotoxins
      a. 2,5
      b. 1,2,3,4,5
      c. 5
      d. 2
      e. 1,2,3,5

2. Endotoxins
   a. all have the same effect.
   b. are found in both Gram-negative and Gram-positive bacteria.
   c. are part of the Gram-positive cell wall only.
   d. are heat labile.
   e. are proteins.

3. Which of the following blood cells are the first to appear in response to an infection?
   a. eosinophils
   b. erythrocytes
   c. lymphocytes
   d. basophils
   e. neutrophils

4. Which of the following nonspecific substances is a normal component of serum?
   a. complement
   b. lysozyme
   c. interferon
   d. collagenase
   e. lysosome

5.Which of the following are ways in which normal flora protect against infection by pathogens?
1. Normal flora provide a surface incompatible for attachment by the invader.
2. Normal flora compete for essential nutrients such as vitamins, amino acids, and iron.
3. Normal flora produce metabolic by-products that are toxic.
4. Normal flora produce lysozyme.
5. There is no evidence that the normal flora protects against infection by pathogens.
  a. 2,3,4
  b. 1,2,3
  c. 1,2,3,4

  d. 4
  e. 5

6. A microroganism that is a commensal
  a. does not receive any benefit from its host.
  b. is harmful to its host.
  c. receives some benefit from its host.

  d. receives benefit at the same time the host benefits too.
  e. None of the above describe a commensal.

REVIEW QUESTIONS

1. Complete the following table by recording a + if the effect of the interaction is positive for either the microorganism or the human. Likewise, record a - if the interaction is negative (i.e., either one suffers from the association). Record a 0 if the interaction is neutral. Give an example of each type of interaction.

INTERACTION	MICROORGANISM	HUMAN	EXAMPLE
COMMENSALISM			
MUTUALISM			
PARASITISM			

2. Distinguish between infection and disease.

3. Explain the statement, "Normal floras are subject to change."

4. List Koch's postulates.

5. Compare and contrast four properties of endotoxins and exotoxins in the following table.

PROPERTY	ENDOTOXINS	EXOTOXINS
1.		
2.		
3.		
4.		

6. Describe how phagocytes destroy microorganisms.

NOTES

ANSWERS:
   Terms and Definitions
      1. receptors 2. symbiosis 3. disease 4. interleukin-1 5. normal flora 6. opportunists 7. virulence 8. infection
      9. transient flora 10. lipid A 11. ligands 12. complement 13. lysosomes 14. pathogen
   Self-Test of Reading Material
      1. b 2. a 3. e 4. a 5. b 6. c

16 IMMUNOLOGY: THE SPECIFIC IMMUNE RESPONSE—ANTIGENS, ANTIBODIES, AND CELL-MEDIATED IMMUNITY

The body's defense against infectious diseases takes two forms: nonspecific resistance mechanisms that act as barriers to infectious agents without regard to the specific organism, and specific immune responses that do depend on the specific organism. The immune response is characterized by its specificity and a memory response. The immune response requires the coordination of a number of cellular and molecular events to provide protection. It is difficult to find a starting place because the events are so closely related. Many aspects of the immune response still remain a mystery, but from what is known, it is an amazing and beautiful process.

KEY CONCEPTS

1. The specific immune response explains why immunity to one disease does not usually confer immunity to another.
2. The specific immune response depends upon two types of lymphocytes interacting with each other and with other cells.
3. The specific immune response has "memory," which enhances the response and rapidly eliminates foreign substances when they are reintroduced into the body. Vaccination takes advantage of this phenomenon.
4. The specific immune response can discriminate between self and nonself.

SUMMARY

I. Innate (Natural) and Acquired Immunity
   A. Innate immunity confers disease resistance that does not involve the production of antibodies or cellular immunity.
   B. Naturally acquired active immunity comes from exposure to antigens in the environment.
   C. Naturally acquired passive immunity involves the transfer of antibodies, such as a mother to her fetus.
   D. Artificially acquired active immunity involves vaccination.
   E. Artificially acquired passive immunity involves preformed antibodies such as immune globulin.

II. The Nonspecific Versus the Specific Immune Response
   A. Nonspecific defenses include physical and physiological barriers, and are found in most of the animal world.
   B. Specific immune response has four features:
      1. Two sets of lymphocytes involved.
      2. Response is highly specific.
      3. Response has memory.
      4. Response is capable of discriminating between self and nonself.

III. Antigens
   A. Antigens are usually macromolecules.
   B. Antigens are usually foreign to the host.
   C. The immune response is directed against antigenic determinants.
   D. Haptens must bind to larger antigenic molecules to induce an immune response.
   E. Most antigens must be processed by antigen-processing cells before they can be involved an immune response.
   F. Most antigens must be associated with products of the major histocompatibility complex (MHC) in order to cause an immune response.

IV. The Duality of the Specific Immune Response
   A. The humoral immune system.
      1. Includes the blood, lymph, and mucus secretions.
      2. Lymphocytes known as B cells produce antibodies.

      B.   The cell-mediated immune system.
         1.   Lymphocytes known as T cells.
         2.   T cells do not secrete antibodies but act directly on other cells.

V.   B Cells and the Antibody Response
      A.   Antibody molecules are proteins known as immunoglobulins.
      B.   Antibody molecules have a Y shape with antigen reaction sites at the ends of the arms of the
      C.   Genes coding for different antibodies achieves antibody diversity through deletions and rearrangements of genetic material in germline cells.
      D.   Antigen-antibody relationships can be likened to a lock and key.
      E.   There are five classes of immunoglobulins:
         1.   IgG is present in the greatest amount and only one that crosses the placenta to protect the fetus and newborn.
         2.   IgM first antibody to form.
         3.   IgA is found mainly on mucous surfaces.
         4.   IgD serves as a specific membrane receptor on B-cells.
         5.   IgE is implicated in allergic reactions.
      F.   Memory cells remain much longer and are primed to respond quickly to antigen.
      G.   Antibody can cause opsonization thereby promoting phagocytosis.

VI.   T cells and Cell-mediated Immunity
      A.   It is the T cell receptor that interacts specifically with the antigenic determinants.
      B.   There are three subpopulations of T cells:
         1.   Helper T cells work with B cells to form an antibody response.
         2.   Cytotoxic T cells kill virus-infected cells and tumor cells.
         3.   Suppresser cells help regulate the immune response.
      C.   Other cells are also involved in cell mediated immunity.
         1.   Killer cells.
         2.   Mononuclear phagocytes and macrophages.

VII.   The Commonalty of the Two Divisions of the Specific Immune Response
      A.   B and T cells have antigen recognition sites on their cell membranes.
      B.   An immune response is triggered if the antigen and recognition site have a close fit.
      C.   Each individual lymphocyte has only a single type of antigen recognition site.
      D.   The immune response depends on clonal expansion of antigenically stimulated lymphocytes.
      E.   Some lymphocytes are live a long time as memory cells, ready to participate in an enhance immune response.

VIII.   The Secondary (Anamnestic) Response and Vaccination
      A.   The anamnestic response depends on memory cells.
      B.   Vaccines are made by inactivation of viruses or by attenuation of viruses or microorganisms.

IX.   Immunological Tolerance
      A.   Recognition of self by the immune system occurs during fetal development.
      B.   Lymphocytes able to bind to self antigens are eliminated before birth.

X.   Regulation of the Immune Response Comes from Suppresser Cells as Well as Feedback Mechanisms.

TERMS AND DEFINITIONS

1. Infectious organisms that are, although still alive, incapable of causing disease are said to be _____.

2. _____ molecules are proteins known as immunoglobulins.

3. A _____ is a group of cells derived from a single cell.

4. Cytotoxic T cells secrete a protein called _____ that makes a hole in the cell membrane of a virus infected cell causing it to lyse and die.

5. _____ are lymphocytes that differentiate into antibody-producing plasma cells on antigenic stimulation.

6. The product of the fusion of a B lymphocyte with a myeloma is called a _____ .

7. _____ are antibodies that coat an antigen and make it more suscetible to phagocytosis.

8. Specific chemical groups on antigens toward which the immune response is directed are

   called _____ .

9. Certain knids of substances that are foreign to the host and are able to trigger an immune response in the host are

   called _____ .

10. _____ are lymphocytes that do not secrete antibodies but instead act directly on other cells.

11. Antibodies belong to the class of serum proteins called _____ .

12. _____ are small molecular weight molecules that must combine with larger molecules such as proteins in order to incite an immune response.

13. The memory response is also known as the _____ response.

14. _____ antibodies are antibodies with a single specificity that are produced by hybridomas.

15. Hormones secreted by lymphocytes that are used as signals for various other cells of the immune system

    are called _____ .

SELF-TEST OF READING MATERIAL

1. Which of the following molecules would be the best antigens?
   a. lipids
   b. glucose
   c. fatty acids
   d. proteins
   e. sugars

2. Which part of the antibody molecule reacts with the antigenic determinants of the antigen?
   a. hinge
   b. H chains
   c. constant sections of the H and L chains
   d. L chains
   e. variable sections of the H and L chains

3. An antigen is
   a. a hapten that combines with an antibody.
   b. a substance that incites an antibody response and can combine specifically with these antibodies.
   c. a small molecule that attaches to cells.
   d. a carbohydrate.
   e. a protein that combines with antibodies.

4. Which of the following best describes some characteristic of B cells?
   a. They differentiate into antibody-producing cells.
   b. They originate in the gut.
   c. They differentiate into neutrophils.
   d. They differentiate and mature in the thymus.
   e. They function in cell-mediated immunity.

5. Which of the following best describes some characteristic of T cells?
    a. They differentiate into antibody-producing cells.
    b. They originate in the gut.
    c. They differentiate into neutrophils.
    d. They differentiate into macrophages.
    e. They function in cell-mediated immunity.

6. The rapid increase and production over a longer period of antibodies in response to a second or subsequent exposure to an antigen is known as
    a. a primary response.
    b. the killer response.
    c. a memory or anamnestic response.
    d. inflammation.
    e. dose response.

7. An immunoglobulin is a(n)
    a. histamine.
    b. antigen.
    c. macrophage.
    d. antibody.
    e. carbohydrate.

8. The portion of an antigen molecule that stimulates an antibody response is called the
    a. antigenic determinant.
    b. epitope.
    c. antibody determinant.
    d. a and b are correct.
    e. b and c are correct.

9. Which of the following classes of immunoglobulins can cross the placenta?
    a. IgG
    b. IgM
    c. IgA
    d. IgD
    e. IgE

10. Macrophages play an important role in the immune response because they present a "processed" antigen to lymphocytes.
    a. True
    b. False

11. Autoimmune diseases result because the immune system fails to recognize host cells as foreign.
    a. True
    b. False

12. Which of the following classes of immunoglobulins are described as secretory?
    a. IgG
    b. IgM
    c. IgA
    d. IgD
    e. IgE

13. Plasma cells are
    a. mature T cells.
    b. immature macrophages.
    c. antibody-producing cells.
    d. mature macrophages.
    e. immature T cells.

14. B lymphocytes originate in
    a. adult bone marrow.
    b. thymus.
    c. fetal liver.
    d. a and b are correct.
    e. a and c are correct.

15. A toxoid is a(n)
    a. type of antibody that combines with a toxin.
    b. type of enzyme that destroys toxins.
    c. inactivated toxin.
    d. type of bacterium that resists phagocytosis.
    e. type of virus.

16. Antibody molecules are
    a. carbohydrates.
    b. lipids.
    c. proteins.
    d. peptidoglycans.

Match the list of types of immunity on the right with the decsriptions on the left.

_____ 17. Immunity after recovery from a disease

_____ 18. Immunity of humans to cat and dog distemper

_____ 19. Administration of gamma globulin for hepatitis

_____ 20. Transfer of immunity from mother to fetus

_____ 21. Immunity after poliovirus vaccine

a. innate
b. naturally acquired active
c. naturally acquired passive
d. artificially acquired active
e. artificially acquired passive

REVIEW QUESTIONS

1. Distinguish among resistance, innate resistance, and acquired immunity.

2. List the types of acquired immunity along with an example of each.

3. List the types of immunoglobulins along with a description of their functions.

4. Describe the types of T cells along with their functions.

NOTES

ANSWERS:

Terms and Definitions

1. attenuated 2. antibodies 3. clone 4. perforin 5. B cells 6. hybridomas 7. opsonins 8. antigenic determinants 9. antigens 10. T cells 11. immunoglobulins 12. haptens 13. anamnestic 14. monoclonal 15. lymphokines

Self-Test of Reading Material

1. d 2. e 3. b 4. a 5. e 6. c 7. d 8. d 9. a 10. a 11. b 12. c 13. c 14. e 15. c 16. c 17. b 18. a 19. e 20. d 21. c

17 IMMUNOLOGY: DISORDERS OF THE IMMUNE SYSTEM

A healthy, effectively functioning immune system is a beautiful thing. Its beauty is because it is a very complicated thing that requires the coordination of many individual parts to protect against infection. Sometimes portions of the system fail and the results can be more detrimental than useful. When the system fails to respond adequately to antigenic stimulation, an immunodeficiency occurs. This failure may be an inherited defect or acquired as in AIDS. At times our immune system appears to over-react to antigenic stimulation and instead of protecting us against certain antigens, it actually causes damage to us. This is the situation known as hypersensitivity or allergies. Finally, in autoimmunity, our immune systems may fail to recognize our own body antigen as self and begin to produce antibodies against our own tissue antigens. All three conditions can have very serious and sometimes devastating effects.

KEY CONCEPTS

1. Immunodeficiency results when the immune system cannot respond adequately to antigenic stimulation.
2. Hypersensitivities result from the immune system reacting inappropriately to certain antigens.
3. Autoimmune disease results from the immune system of the body responding to its own tissues as foreign.
4. A number of diagnostic tests rely on immune responses to antigens.

SUMMARY

I. Immunodeficiency Diseases
   A. Primary immunodeficiency disease.
      1. Occurs because of genetic defect.
      2. In DiGeorge syndrome, the thymus fails to develop and patient lacks T lymphocytes.
      3. X-linked agammaglobulinemia patients lack B lymphocytes.
      4. In severe combined immunodeficiency disease the bone marrow stem cells are defective.
      5. Chediak-Higashi disease affects the phagocytes.
   B. Secondary immunodeficiency disease.
      1. Acquired as the result of infection, aging, or other factors.
      2. Multiple myelomas are cancers.
      3. Acquired Immune Deficiency Disease (AIDS)
         a. Caused by HIV virus, a retrovirus.
         b. Virus kills T-helper lymphocytes.
         c. Body susceptible to opportunistic infections.

II. Hypersensitivities
   A. Type I hypersensitivity is an IgE-mediated reaction.
      1. IgE antibodies attach to receptors on mast cells and basophils.
      2. When antigen combines with these cell-fixed IgE antibodies, histamine and other chemical mediators are released.
      3. IgE-mediated skin reactions such as hives are produced.
      4. Localized anaphylaxis such as hayfever and asthma are IgE-mediated respiratory reactions.
      5. Generalized anaphylaxis can occur after a bee sting or penicillin reaction.
      6. Immunotherapy involves repeatedly injecting a small but increasing amount of the offending antigen in order to elicit an IgG response.
   B. Type II hypersensitivity or cytotoxic reactions are caused by humoral antibodies that destroy normal cells.
      1. Complement-fixing antibodies react with cell surface antigens and cause injury or death to cells.
      2. Transfusion reactions.
         a. ABO blood group system.
         b. ABO antigens are polysaccharides on the red blood cells.

      3. Hemolytic disease of newborns.
         a. Rh or (rhesus) blood group system is involved.
         b. If an Rh-negative mother carries an Rh-positive fetus, the Rh-positive cells cause antibody production in the mother. These antibodies can cross the placenta and destroy fetal red blood cells.
         c. A new treatment involves injecting anti-Rh antibodies into the mother shortly after delivery or abortion to develop anti-Rh antibodies.

  C. Type III hypersensitivity or immune complexes activate inflammatory mechanisms
      1. Immune complexes have considerable biological activity such as blood clotting mechanisms, attraction of polymorphonuclear leukocytes, and stimulation of lysosomal enzyme release.
      2. Immune complexes can be deposited in kidneys, joints, and skin.
      3. Arthus reaction is the death of tissue following injection of antigen into previously immunized animal.
      4. Other diseases, such as serum sickness and farmer's lung, involve immune complexes.

  D. Type IV Hypersensitivity or Delayed Hypersensitivity involves T cells and cell-mediated immunity.
      1. The response develops slowly over a few days.
      2. Tuberculin skin test is an example of delayed hypersensitivity.
      3. Contact allergies are reactions to metals, poison ivy, and other substances.
      4. Delayed hypersensitivity is involved in infectious diseases.
         a. Leprosy and hepatitis are examples.
         b. Cell destruction with impairment of tissue function is involved.

  E. Antigenic incompatibility leads to tissue graft rejection.
      1. MHC matching essential to avoid rejection.
      2. Use of immunosuppressant drugs, such as cyclosporin, has helped keep graft rejection under control.
      3. Immunity to cancer cells sometimes breaks down.

III. Autoimmune Diseases
  A. Some, such as myesthenia gravis, are due to the production of humoral antibodies
  B. Some, such as sympathetic ophthalmia, are due to delayed hypersensitivity reactions.

IV. Immunological Diagnostic Testing Techniques
  A. Precipitation reactions, including the Ouchterlony technique and immune electrophoresis, involve soluble antigen.
  B. Agglutination reactions are similar to precipitin reactions except they involve particulate antigen.
  C. Complement fixation test uses antibody-sensitized red blood cells to detect the presence of complement and cause cell lysis.
  D. Virus neutralization test.
  E. Direct and indirect immunofluorescence tests.
  F. Radioimmunoassay (RIA) and enzyme-linked imunosorbent assay (ELISA).

SELF-TEST OF READING MATERIAL

1. An exaggerated or inappropriate immune response is known as a(n)
    a. immunodeficiency.
    b. precipitation.
    c. histamine.
    d. hypersensitivity.
    e. allergen.

2. Localized anaphylaxis involving the skin is called
    a. hay fever.
    b. asthma.
    c. shock.
    d. hives.
    e. hayfever.

3. Immunotherapy to prevent generalized anaphylaxis is done by injecting dilute doses of
    a. IgG antibodies.
    b. antihistamine.
    c. IgE antibodies.
    d. offending antigen.
    e. offending antibody.

4. Which of the following is most commonly involved in graft rejections?
   a. ABO antigens
   b. ABO antibodies
   c. MHC antigens
   d. MHC antibodies
   e. a and c are correct.

5. Which of the following would be a Type IV, or delayed hypersensitivity?
   a. hayfever
   b. allergic contact dermatitis
   c. glomerulonephritis
   d. penicillin reaction
   e. blood transfusion reaction

6. The symptoms of an immune complex reaction are due to
   a. an inflammatory response.
   b. histamines.
   c. autoimmune antigens.
   d. IgE.
   e. autoimmune antibodies.

7. Autoimmunity is a delayed hypersensitivity or Type IV reaction.
   a. True
   b. False

8. Allergic contact dermatitis is mediated by
   a. sensitized T cells.
   b. IgG antibodies.
   c. IgE antibodies.
   d. basophils and mast cells.
   e. sensitized macrophages.

9. A hypersensitive reaction occurs
   a. during the first exposure to an antigen.
   b. in individuals with diseases of the immune system.
   c. on a second or subsequent exposure to an antigen.
   d. during autoimmune diseases.
   e. in immunologically-deficient individuals.

10. Type I hypersensitivities
    1. are cell-mediated.
    2. are IgE-mediated.
    3. have many symptoms that are due to histamine.
    4. are caused by antibodies are bound to basophils and mast cells.
    5. have symptoms that occur soon after exposure to the allergen.
    a. 1,4,5
    b. 2,3,4,5
    c. 1
    d. 2,4,5
    e. 1,3,4,5

11. Hemolytic disease of the newborn occurs when an
    a. Rh-positive mother carries an Rh-negative fetus.
    b. O mother carries an AB fetus.
    c. Rh-negative mother carries an Rh-positive fetus
    d. AB mother carries an O fetus.
    e. Two of the above are correct.

12. Reaction of antigen with IgE antibodies attached to mast cells causes
    a. precipitation.
    b. complement fixation.
    c. degranulation.
    d. agglutination.
    e. asthma.

13. Immediate hypersensitivities are mediated by
    a. allergens.
    b. macrophages.
    c. humoral antibodies
    d. antigens.
    e. T cells.

14. Immunotherapy for hypersensitivities probably works because of
    a. the production of IgG blocking antibodies.
    b. development of suppresser T cells.
    c. saturation of IgE antibodies.
    d. All of the above are correct.
    e. Only a and b are correct.

15. Delayed hypersensitivities are mediated by
    a. allergens.
    b. macrophages.
    c. humoral antibodies.
    d. antigens.
    e. T cells.

16. Farmer's lung is the result of
    a. sensitized T cells.
    b. immune complex reactions.
    c. Type I hypersensitivity.
    d. cytotoxic reactions.
    e. urticaria.

17. Autoimmune diseases result when the immune response recognizes host cells as antigenic.
    a. True
    b. False

18. Which of the following techniques are based on precipitation reactions?
    a. Ouchterlony technique
    b. immunoelectrophoresis
    c. countercurrent immunoelectrophoresis
    d. All of the above are correct.
    e. Only a and c are correct.

19. Precipitation reactions involve particulate antigens while agglutination reactions involve soluble antigens.
    a. True
    b. False

20. Hemagglutination tests involve clumping of
    a. chicken cells.
    b. red blood cells.
    c. antibodies.
    d. viruses.
    e. lymphocytes.

REVIEW QUESTIONS

1. Distinguish between primary (or congenital) and secondary (or acquired) immunodeficiency disease.

2. What conditions can cause secondary or acquired immunodeficiency disease.

3. Give an example of an immunodeficiency disease that involves each of the following:

    a. B cell deficiency

    b. T cell deficiency

    c. B and T cell deficiency

    d. defective phagocyte

4. Describe for each of the above conditions what would be missing in the immune response.

5. Distinguish between precipitation and agglutination reactions.

ANSWERS:
  Self-Test of Reading Material
    1. d 2. d 3. d 4. c 5. b 6. a 7. b 8. a 9. c 10. b 11. c 12. c 13. c 14. e 15. e 16. b 17. a 18. d 19. b
    20. b

NOTES

18 EPIDEMIOLOGY AND PUBLIC HEALTH

Epidemiology is the study of factors that influence the frequency and distribution of diseases. Exactly what does that mean? It means that epidemiologists are like detectives because they try to predict when an epidemic is occurring or is going to occur. They look for clues related to the number of new cases of a disease compared to its usual numbers. They look for clues as to where the epidemic started, where it will spread, and who are most likely to get the disease. From this information, public health services can try to interrupt the transmission of the disease by appropriate means. Epidemiologists need a lot of math and statistical training in addition to microbiology.

KEY CONCEPTS

1. Today's public health system depends on advanced technology, social organization, and political stability.
2. Identifying the origin of an epidemic depends on a careful comparison of the characteristics and activities of those affected and unaffected by the epidemic.
3. Different infectious agents can produce the same symptoms, and the same infectious agent can produce different symptoms.
4. Different strains within the same species of potential pathogen can differ markedly in virulence and pathogenicity.
5. Asymptomatic carriers of an infectious agent can be responsible for epidemics.
6. In epidemics where most infections are asymptomatic, the extent of spread of the causative agent can be far greater than indicated by the number of ill people.
7. Infectious agents with a long incubation period can spread widely before an epidemic is detected.
8. The smaller the infecting dose of a pathogen, the longer the incubation period, and the greater the likelihood of asymptomatic infection.

SUMMARY

I. Epidemiology Is the Study of Factors Influencing the Frequency and Distribution of Disease
    A. An epidemic is an unusually large number of cases in a population.
    B. Sporadic cases representing the usual incidence is known as endemic.
    C. A pandemic is a world wide epidemic.

II. Infectious Disease Epidemics, Origin and Spread
    A. The cause or origin is determined by first defining the characteristics of the people (population) involved.
    B. The infectious agent must be precisely identified.
        1. Bacteriophage typing is based on viral specificity—*Staphylococcus*.
        2. Bacteriocin typing—*Pseudomonas* species.
        3. Antibiograms.
        4. Biotyping and serotyping.
        5. Electrophoresis of endonuclease digests—herpes simplex virus.
    C. The reservoir of an infectious agent is the sum of its potential sources.
    D. Factors in the spread of epidemics.
        1. Vectors and vehicles.
        2. Use of sentinels.
        3. Incubation period.
    E. Airborne spread of infectious disease.
    F. Food and water in the transmission of infectious disease
        1. Multiplication of the pathogen in food.
        2. Long incubation and asymptomatic infections with water-borne pathogens.
    G. Person-to-person transmission.
        1. Contamination of hands by fomites, respiratory secretions, feces.
        2. Carriers.

III. Population Characteristics
  A. Age—prior exposure.
  B. Genetic background—malaria resistance among black people.
  C. Nutrition, crowding, and cultural factors.

IV. The Infecting Agent
  A. Microbial virulence—bacterial meningitis.
  B. Intensity of exposure—role of the infectious dose.

V. Approaches to Control of Infectious Diseases
  A. Promotion of good general health.
    1. Adequate rest, nutrition, exercise, freedom from stress.
    2. Active immunization.
  B. Reducing the reservoir and interrupting transmission.

VI. Hospital Epidemiology
  A. Nosocomial infections.
    1. Unusually susceptible population.
    2. Presence of virulent pathogen.
    3. Carriers among hospital staff.
    4. Potential of disease transmission to the outside community.
  B. Hospital epidemiologist.

VII. Infectious Disease Control Network
  A. Schools, microbiology laboratories, news media.
    1. Governmental public health laboratories.
  B. National Centers for Disease Control and Prevention and the World Health Organization.
    1. Studies.
    2. Infection control teams.
    3. Assistance to laboratories.

TERMS AND DEFINITIONS

_____ 1. An unusually large number of cases of a disease occurring in a given population

_____ 2. Infections contracted while a person is in the hospital

_____ 3. All of the places where an infectious agent is found

_____ 4. Scattered cases of disease occurring in a population over a long period

_____ 5. Inanimate objects that can serve to transmit infections

_____ 6. Viruses that are used to identify bacterial strains

_____ 7. Food and other nonliving materials that may spread infections

_____ 8. The first person to have a disease in an epidemic

a. epidemic
b. nosocomial infection
c. pandemic
d. carrier
e. endemic
f. fomites
g. epidemiology
h. attack rates
i. bacteriophage typing
j. index case
k. antibiograms
l. sentinel
m. biotyping
n. vehicles
o. reservoirs
p. vectors

_____ 9. The study of the factors that influence the frequency and distribution of disease

_____ 10. An apparently healthy individual who harbors a pathogen

_____ 11. Antibiotic susceptibility patterns used to identify strains of bacteria

_____ 12. A world-wide epidemic

_____ 13. Insects or other animals that may spread disease

_____ 14. Using patterns of biochemical activity to identify bacterial strains

_____ 15. The number of cases developing per hundred people exposed

_____ 16. A chicken, for example, used to detect the presence of encephalitis-infected mosquitoes

SELF-TEST OF READING MATERIAL

1. The study of when diseases occur and how they are transmitted is called
   a. a public health survey.
   b. epidemiology.
   c. ecology.
   d. the Centers for Disease Control.
   e. diagnostic microbiology.

2. Fomites are
   a. insect vectors.
   b. animate objects.
   c. an ancient tribe of Israel.
   d. inanimate objects.
   e. biological vectors.

3. A nosocomial infection is an infection
   a. that can come from the patient's own normal flora.
   b. acquired during hospitalization.
   c. always caused by medical personnel.
   d. a and b are correct.
   e. b and c are correct.

4. Which of the following are reservoirs for human infections.
   a. food and water
   b. humans
   c. animals
   d. All of the above are reservoirs for human infections.
   e. Only b and c are reservoirs.

5. A simple method for interrupting the person-to-person transmission of disease is
   a. immunization
   b. handwashing
   c. prophylactic chemotherapy
   d. isolation
   e. quarantine

6. Water-borne pathogens tend to be intestinal organisms.
   a. True
   b. False

7. Factors within a population that can influence the characteristic of an epidemic are
   1. age
   2. prior exposure
   3. crowding
   4. nutrition
   5. genetic background
   6. cultural factors

   a. 1,5
   b. 1,2,4,5
   c. 1,2,3,4,5
   d. All of the above.
   e. None of the above because only microbial factors can influence the characteristics of an epidemic.

8. A human carrier does not have an infection but simply spreads a disease through mechanical transmission.
   a. True
   b. False

9. People get diseases mostly from
   a. their pets.
   b. water.
   c. other people.
   d. food.
   e. air

10. Droplet nuclei are significant in the transmission of diseases of the
    a. digestive system.
    b. reproductive system.
    c. nervous system.
    d. respiratory system.
    e. skin.

REVIEW QUESTIONS

1. Distinguish among the terms vector, vehicle, carrier, and reservoir.

2. Describe the six components of body substance isolation.

3. Why are carriers such a public health problem?

4. Give two reasons why the attack rates for food-borne infections are usually much higher than those for water-borne infections.

5. Choose three characteristics of human populations that influence the nature of epidemics and give a brief explanation as to why.

ANSWERS:
  Terms and Definitions
   1. a 2. b 3. o 4. e 5. f 6. i 7. n 8. j 9. g 10. d 11. k 12. c 13. p 14. m 15. h 16. l
  Self-Test of Reading Material
   1. b 2. d 3. d 4. d 5. b 6. a 7. d 8. b 9. c 10. d

NOTES

19 SKIN INFECTIONS

We usually do not think of it in that way, but our skin is our largest organ. It is the boundary between our body and the outside world. We all learned in sixth grade hygiene class that our skin was our first line of defense against infection. This chapter describes a few of the things that can invade and colonize our body when the skin barrier is broken. In a few instances the skin is attacked from the inside by organisms entering through the respiratory or digestive systems. You will be introduced to your skin and its normal flora so that you will have a better appreciation of the truly remarkable job it does for you every day.

KEY CONCEPTS

1. The skin is a large complex organ covering the external body surface.
2. Properties of the skin cause it to resist microbial colonization, provide a physical barrier to the entry of potential pathogens, and assist the body's regulation of temperature and fluid balance.
3. The changes in the skin during an infectious disease commonly reflect disease involvement of other parts of the body.

SUMMARY

I. Anatomy and Physiology
   A. The skin repels potential pathogens by being tough, dry, acidic, and toxic.

II. The Normal Flora Of Human Skin Consistently Includes Three Groups Of Microorganisms
   A. Diphtheroids are Gram-positive, pleomorphic, rod-shaped bacteria.
      1. Growth of *Propionibacterium acnes* is enhanced by oily secretion of sebaceous glands. *P. acnes* produces fatty acids from the gland secretion. They are usually anaerobes, but some are able to tolerate growth in air.
   B. Staphylococci are Gram-positive cocci that help prevent colonization by potential pathogens and maintain the balance among flora of the skin.
      1. *Staphylococcus epidermidis* is universally present on the skin and is pathogenic at times.
   C. *Malassezia* species, single-celled yeasts found universally on the skin, probably cause some cases of dandruff as well as tinea versicolor, and more serious rashes in AIDS patients.

III. Skin Diseases Caused by Bacteria
   A. Furuncles and carbuncles are caused by *Staphylococcus aureus,* which is coagulase positive and is often resistant to penicillin and other antibiotics. Carbuncles are dangerous because the infection is more likely to be carried to heart, brain, or bones.
   B. Staphylococcal scalded skin syndrome results from exotoxins produced by certain strains of *Staphylococcus aureus.*
   C. Impetigo is a superficial skin infection caused by *Staphylococcus aureus* and *Streptococcus pyogenes.*
      1. The capsule and the M-protein of the cell wall of S. *pyogenes* interfere with phagocytosis, thus aiding pathogenesis.
      2. Penicillin or erythromycin is effective in most S. *pyogenes* infections.
      3. Acute glomerulonephritis, a kidney disease, is a complication of S. *pyogenes* infections.
   D. Rocky Mountain spotted fever (RMSF), caused by the obligate intracellular bacterium, *Rickettsia rickettsii,* is transmitted to humans by the bite of an infected tick. Tetracycline or chloramphenicol is used in treatment of RMSF.
   E. Lyme disease can imitate many other diseases. It is caused by a spirochete, *Borrelia burgdorferi* and is transmitted to humans by ticks. Erythema chronicum migrans is the hallmark of the disease. Doxycycline, amoxicillin, and erythromycin are effective in treating early stages of the disease.

IV. Skin Diseases Caused by Viruses
   A. Chicken pox is a common disease of childhood caused by the varicella-zoster virus, a member of the herpesvirus family.
      1. Herpes zoster, or "shingles," can occur months or years after chicken pox and represents a reactivation of a varicella virus infection in the distribution of a sensory nerve.
      2. Herpes zoster cases can be responsible for chicken pox epidemics.
   B. Rubeola (measles) is a potentially dangerous viral disease that can be fatal in some cases and can lead to serious secondary bacterial infections in others.
      1. Rubeola can be controlled by immunizing young children and susceptible adults with a live attenuated vaccine. A two-dose regimen is now employed in an effort to decrease the size of the non-immune population.
   C. Rubella (three day measles, German measles) contracted by a woman in the first eight weeks of pregnancy results in at least a 90% chance of congenital rubella syndrome. Immunization with a live virus protects against this disease, but many women still reach childbearing age without proper vaccination.
   D. Numerous viruses can cause rashes. In recent years the viral cause of two exanthems has been determined.
      1. Erythema infectiosum is characterized by a "slapped cheek" rash. It is caused by parvovirus B-19.
      2. Exanthem subitum is characterized by several days of high fever and transitory rash appearing as the temperature returns to normal. The disease is caused by human herpesvirus, type 6.
   E. Warts are skin tumors caused by a number of papillomaviruses. They are generally benign, but some genital warts have been associated with cancer of the uterine cervix.

V. Skin Diseases Caused by Fungi
   A. Invasive skin infections are sometimes caused by the yeast, *Candida albicans*.
   B. Athlete's foot and ringworm are caused by certain species of mold-type fungi which feed on keratin-containing cells.

TERMS AND DEFINITIONS

1. _____ is an oily secretion produced by glands in the skin that empty into the sides of the hair follicles.

2. Skin rashes are also called _____ .

3. _____ is a cell wall component of virtually all strains of *Staphylococcus aureus* and binds to the Fc portion of antibody molecules.

4. A skin infection characterized by superficial pus-filled blisters is called _____ .

5. _____ is the surface layer of the skin that is composed of scaly material.

6. A penicillin-destroying enzyme produced by many strains of *Staphylococcus aureus* is _____ .

7. A _____ is a disease that exists primarily in animals other than humans, but that can be transmitted to humans.

8. Skin-invading molds are collectively called _____ .

9. A cell wall component of *Streptococcus pyogenes* that inhibits phagocytosis is _____ .

10. _____ is an enzyme that causes plasma to coagulate and is used to identify pathogenic

   strains of _____ .

SELF-TEST OF READING MATERIAL

Match the condition on the left with its etiological agent on the right. A condition may have more than one causative agent and an agent may cause more than one condition.

_____ 1. furuncle

_____ 2. warts

_____ 3. scalded skin syndrome

_____ 4. fifth disease

_____ 5. chicken pox

_____ 6. food poisoning

_____ 7. subacute sclerosing panencephalitis

_____ 8. impetigo

_____ 9. measles

_____ 10. scarlet fever

_____ 11. shingles

_____ 12. toxic shock syndrome

_____ 13. Lyme disease

_____ 14. glomerulonephritis

_____ 15. Rocky mountain spotted fever

a. *Staphylococcus aureus*
b. papillomavirus
c. B-19
d. *Streptococcus pyogenes*
e. Rubeola
f. *Rickettsia rickettsii*
g. Herpes zoster
h. *Borrelia burgdoferi*
i. Varicella zoster

16. The layer of skin that contains many nerves, blood vessels, and lymphatic vessels is the
    a. epidermis.
    b. dermis.
    c. hypodermis.
    d. keratin.
    e. scaly layer.

17. Vaccination of infants against rubeola is done at about 15 months of age because of
    a. placentally transferred maternal antigens.
    b. infant antibodies.
    c. it is easier to give the injection.
    d. infant antigens.
    e. placentally transferred maternal antibodies.

18. Which of the following allows *Staphylococcus aureus* to colonize oily hair follicles?
    a. lipase
    b. protein A
    c. collagenase
    d. coagulase
    e. hyaluronidase

19. An epidermolytic toxin is involved in
    a. chicken pox.
    b. shingles.
    c. scalded skin syndrome.
    d. exanthem subitum.
    e. warts.

20. Lyme disease is a tick-borne disease with similarities to syphilis.
    a. True
    b. False

REVIEW QUESTIONS

1. Describe, in addition to protection against infection, six other functions of the skin.

2. Give four characteristics of skin that help it resist infection.

3. How does the normal flora of the skin help protect against infection?

4. Describe four extracellular products of *Staphylococcus aureus* and how they contribute to its virulence.

5. Rocky Mountain spotted fever and Lyme disease share some common features. Describe two they have in common.

6. What is the relationship between varicella and herpes zoster?

7. How are warts transmitted?

ANSWERS:

Terms and Definitions

1. sebum 2. exanthems 3. protein A 4. pyoderma 5. epidermis 6. penicillinase 7. zoonosis 8. dermatophytes 9. M protein 10. coagulase/*Staphylococcus aureus*

Self-Test of Reading Material

1. a 2. b 3. a 4. c 5. i 6. a 7. e 8. a,d 9. e 10. d 11. g 12. a 13. h 14. d 15. f 16. b 17. e 18. a 19. c 20. a

NOTES

20 UPPER RESPIRATORY SYSTEM INFECTIONS

We all know that treating a cold will cause it to go away in seven days but if you leave it alone it will disappear in a week. Like colds, most upper respiratory infections are not life-threatening, but can be extremely uncomfortable and irritating. We take into our lungs very large volumes of air each day and some of that air will contain infectious agents. Our upper respiratory tract is a marvel at preventing infections, most of the time. When we compromise the barriers that our system provides with such abuse as smoking and narcotics, we make ourselves more susceptible to infection. Serious infections such as diphtheria can be controlled by immunization but strep throat must be treated to prevent serious sequellae.

KEY CONCEPTS

1. Untreated skin or throat infections by *Streptococcus pyogenes* can occasionally result in serious kidney or heart damage even though these organs are not infected. The damage is probably caused by the immune system.
2. Some diseases arise because an exotoxin is absorbed from a localized infection. The toxin then circulates throughout the body causing damage to tissues some distance from the site of infection.
3. Circulating toxins may not affect all tissues equally. A toxin may target specific organs because it attaches to receptors on the cells of the organ.
4. Many different kinds of infectious agents can produce the same symptoms and signs of disease.

SUMMARY

I. Anatomy and Physiology
   A. The moist linings of the eyes, the nasolacrimal duct, the middle ears, sinuses, mastoid air cells, nose, and throat comprise the main structures of the upper respiratory system.
   B. An important defense system is the movement of mucus by the ciliated cells that line much of the respiratory system. The middle ears and sinuses are usually kept free of microorganisms by this mechanism.
   C. The functions of the upper respiratory tract include temperature and humidity regulation of inspired air and removal of microorganisms.

II. Normal Flora
   A. Secretions of the nasal entrance are often colonized by diphtheroids, micrococci, and *Staphylococcus aureus* (coagulase-positive staphylococci).
   B. The nasopharyngeal flora includes alpha-hemolytic streptococci, nonhemolytic streptococci, *Moraxella (Branhamella) catarrhalis,* diphtheroids, and anaerobes of the genus *Bacteroides.*

III. Bacterial Infections
   A. *Streptococcus pyogenes* causes strep throat, a very important bacterial infection. Infection may lead to scarlet fever, rheumatic fever, or glomerulonephritis.
   B. Diphtheria, caused by *Corynebacterium diphtheriae,* is a toxin-mediated disease that can be prevented by immunization.
   C. Otitis media and sinusitis develop when infection extends from the nasopharynx.
   D. Conjunctivitis (pink eye) is usually caused by *Haemophilus influenzae* or *S. pneumoniae* . Viral causes, including adenoviruses and rhinoviruses, usually result in a milder illness.

IV. Viral Infections
   A. The common cold can be caused by many different viruses, rhinoviruses being the most common.
   B. Adenoviruses cause illnesses varying from mild to severe, which may resemble a common cold or strep throat.

SELF-TEST OF READING MATERIAL

1. Which of the following is a serious complication that may develop after recovery from strep throat?
   a. scarlet fever
   b. acute glomerulonephritis
   c. rheumatic fever
   d. a and b are correct.
   e. b and c are correct.

2. The rash of scarlet fever is caused by
   a. an erythrogenic toxin.
   b. bacteria in the skin.
   c. high fever.
   d. a virus.
   e. an allergy.

3. A toxoid is a(n)
   a. antibody against a toxin.
   b. inactivated toxin.
   c. larger molecular weight toxin.
   d. small molecular weight toxin.
   e. Two of the above are correct.

4. Tonsils are lymphoid tissue and important producers of immunity to infectious agents.
   a. True
   b. False

5. Which of the following will interfere with normal ciliary action of the respiratory epithelium and make an individual more susceptible to infection?
   a. viral infection
   b. alcohol
   c. narcotics
   d. tobacco
   e. All of the above promote infection.

6. Most strains of *Streptococcus pyogenes* produce ß-hemolysis on blood agar plates from the activity of two hemolytic enzymes that are sensitive to oxygen.
   a. True
   b. False

7. New tests for strep throat that are rapid and can be performed in a physician's office rely on *Streptococcus pyogenes*
   a. antibodies in the throat.
   b. antigens in the blood.
   c. cultivation.
   d. antibodies in the blood.
   e. antigens in the throat.

8. Acute glomerulonephritis, a consequence of strep throat infections, is actually caused by
   a. immune complexes in the kidneys.
   b. *Streptococcus pyogenes* endotoxins.
   c. immune complexes in the throat.
   d. *Streptococcus pyogenes* exotoxins.
   e. a and d are correct.

9. Which of the following is most seriously affected by rheumatic fever.
   a. heart
   b. kidney
   c. brain
   d. liver
   e. throat

10. Depletion of which of the following enhances toxin synthesis in *Corynebacterium diphtheriae*?
    a. oxygen
    b. serum
    c. iron
    d. vitamins
    e. carbon dioxide

11. *Streptococcus pneumoniae* and *Haemophilius influenzae* are the most important bacterial pathogens associated with otitis media or middle ear infection.
    a. True
    b. False

12. *Streptococcus pneumoniae* and *Haemophilius influenzae* are common causes of bacterial conjuctivitis or pink eye.
    a. True
    b. False

REVIEW QUESTIONS

1. List the genera of normal flora of the upper respiratory tract. Identify and name those that contain pathogenic species.

2. Explain the designation of *Streptococcus pyogenes* as the "group A ß-hemolytic strep."

3. *Streptococcus pyogenes* cannot be isolated from patients with acute glomerulonephritis or rheumatic fever but it is still considered the "cause" of these conditions. Explain this observation.

4. Give two examples of diseases whose symptoms are caused by exotoxins produced by lysogenized bacterial cells. Also, write the correct scientific name of each of the causative agents.

119

5. What are the functions of the A and the B fragment of the diphtheria toxin?

6. Why is a vaccine against *Streptococcus pyogenes* unlikely?

ANSWERS:
Self-Test of Reading Material
  1. e 2. a 3. b 4. a 5. e 6. b 7. e 8. a 9. a 10. c 11. a 12. a

21 LOWER RESPIRATORY SYSTEM INFECTIONS

The lower respiratory tract is usually considered free from normal flora and usually only contains relatively few transient organisms that have been inhaled. Infection of the lower respiratory tract is known generally as pneumonia and can be caused by bacterial, viral, and fungal agents. Other irritations, such as those from chemicals, are also referred to as pneumonias. Many diseases, such as measles and chicken pox, first enter our body through the respiratory system and are often spread to others by respiratory droplets. In addition to several bacterial pneumonias, other serious diseases of the lower respiratory tract include tuberculosis, legionnaires' disease, and pertussis.

KEY CONCEPTS

1. Very efficient mechanisms protect the lower respiratory system; bacterial lung infections usually occur only in people whose defenses are impaired.
2. Most pneumonias are bacterial or viral, but eukaryotic microorganisms, chemicals, and allergies can also cause pneumonias.
3. A vaccine composed of killed organisms can confer protection against some Gram-negative bacterial diseases such as pertussis.
4. Most *Mycobacterium tuberculosis* infections become latent, posing a risk of reactivation throughout life.
5. Most deaths from influenza are caused by secondary bacterial infections.
6. The host's immune system can play a key role in the pathogenesis of lung disease.

SUMMARY

I. Anatomy and Physiology
   A. The lower respiratory system includes the trachea, bronchi, bronchioles, and alveoli. Pleural membranes cover the lungs and line the chest cavity.
   B. Ciliated cells line much of the respiratory tract and remove microorganisms by constantly propelling mucus out of the respiratory system.

II. Bacterial Pneumonias
   A. Bacterial pneumonias can be caused by Gram-positive and Gram-negative organisms, and one species of *Mycoplasma.*
      1. *Streptococcal pneumoniae* is one of the most common causes of pneumonia. The bacterium is also known as the pneumococcus.
      2. *Klebsiella pneumoniae may* cause permanent damage to the lung. Serious complications are more common than with other bacterial pneumonias. Treatment is more difficult, partly because klebsiellae often contain R factor plasmids.
      3. *Mycoplasma pneumonia* is often mild and referred to as "walking pneumonia." Serious complications are rare. Penicillins and cephalosporins are not useful in treatment because *M. pneumoniae* lacks a cell wall. Cold agglutinins often help confirm the diagnosis.

III. Other Bacterial Infections of the Lung
   A. Whooping cough (pertussis) is characterized by violent spasms of coughing and gasping. The cause is a Gram-negative rod, *Bordetella pertussis.* Childhood immunization prevents the disease.
   B. Tuberculosis is generally slowly progressive or heals and remains latent, presenting the risk of reactivation. The cause is an acid-fast rod, *Mycobacterium tuberculosis.*
   C. Legionnaires' disease occurs when there is a high infecting dose of the causative microorganisms or underlying lung disease. The cause, *Legionella pneumophila,* is a rod-shaped bacterium common in the environment. It requires special stains and culture techniques for diagnosis.

IV. Influenza: A Lower Respiratory Tract Disease Caused by Orthomyxoviruses.
   A. Serious epidemics are characteristic of influenza A viruses. Antigenic shifts and drifts are responsible.
   B. Deaths are usually but not always caused by secondary infection.
   C. Antibody against hemagglutinin gives protection.
   D. Reye's syndrome may rarely occur during recovery from influenza B and other viral infections, but is probably not caused by the virus itself.

V. Fungal Infections of the Lung
   A. Coccidioidomycosis occurs in hot, dry areas of the Western Hemisphere. The airborne spores of the dimorphic soil fungus, *Coccidioides immitis,* initiate the infection.
   B. Histoplasmosis is similar to coccidioidomycosis but occurs in tropical and temperate zones. The causative fungus, *Histoplasma capsulatum,* is dimorphic and found in soils contaminated by bat or bird droppings.

TERMS AND DEFINITIONS

1. Tiny liquid or solid particles suspended in air and are often highly contagious are called _____ .

2. _____ is a thick discharge that accumulates during respiratory disease and consists of mucus and a variety of cells.

3. A purified protein fraction isolated from *Mycobacterium tuberculosis* and used to test for cases of tuberculosis is

   called _____ and the test is known as the _____ test.

4. _____ are infections caused by fungi.

5. The glycoprotein spikes on the outer membranes of influenza viruses are called _____

   and _____ .

6. Vaccines that contain the antigens that stimulate immunity but lack other components of the bacterial cell

   are called _____ vaccines.

7. Histoplasmosis has been called the _____ disease because cave explorers are at a risk for contracting the condition.

8. _____ and _____ are types of genetic variation that are responsible for changes in the antigens of influenza viruses.

9. The granulomas of tuberculosis are called _____ , which in some cases cause the

   death of the tissue and form a cheesy material by a process called _____ .

10. An inflammation of the layers that surround the lungs is called _____ .

SELF-TEST OF READING MATERIAL

1. Walking pneumonia is caused by
   a. *Mycoplasma tuberculosis.*
   b. *Mycobacterium pneumoniae.*
   c. *Klebsiella pneumoniae.*
   d. *Mycobacterium tuberculosis.*
   e. *Mycoplasma pneumoniae.*

2. Histoplasmosis is associated with the growth of *Histoplasma capsulatum* in
   a. soil containing bird and bat droppings.
   b. dust and dry air.
   c. plants.
   d. hospitals.
   e. nasal secretions.

3. Deaths from influenza are most often due to
   a. heart failure.
   b. secondary bacterial infections.
   c. exotoxins.
   d. kidney failure.
   e. suffocation.

4. Which of the following organisms grows naturally inside amoebas as well as body phagocytes?
   a. *Mycobacterium tuberculosis*
   b. *Mycoplasma pneumoniae*
   c. influenza A
   d. *Legionella pneumophila*
   e. *Klebsiella pneumoniae*

5. *Mycoplasma pneumoniae* infections are most common in
   a. people over the age of 40.
   b. infants.
   c. adolescents.
   d. people over the age of 60.
   e. people between 40 and 60.

6. Infection with *Bordetella* pertussis is confined to lobes of the lungs.
   a. True
   b. False

7. Person-to-person transmission is not characteristic of infections caused by
   a. *Legionella pneumophila*
   b. *Mycoplasma pneumoniae*
   c. influenza A
   d. *Klebsiella pneumoniae*
   e. *Mycobacterium tuberculosis*

8. Reye's syndrome sometimes occurs with infections of influenza B.
   a. True
   b. False

9. The "P" in DPT is
   a. attenuated *Bordetella pertussis*
   b. pertussis exotoxin.
   c. killed *Bordetella pertussis.*
   d. pertussis endotoxin.
   e. toxoid.

10. *Mycobacterium tuberculosis* endospores are readily killed by pasteurization.
    a. True
    b. False

REVIEW QUESTIONS

1. Why is the BCG vaccine not used in AIDS patients?

2. Why is "walking" pneumonia not treated with penicillin?

3. What accounts for the "swine" in swine flu?

4. Why did it take several months to discover the agent that was responsible for the outbreak of Legionnaires' disease in 1976?

5. What factors are contributing to the increase of tuberculosis?

6. How do alcoholism and cigarette smoking predispose a person to pneumonia?

ANSWERS:
  Terms and Definitions
    1. aerosols 2. sputum 3. tuberculin/Mantoux 4. mycoses 5. hemagglutinin/neuraminidase 6. acellular
    7. spelunker 8. antigenic drift/antigenic shift 9. tubercules/caseous necrosis 10. pleurisy
  Self-Test of Reading Material
    1. e 2. a 3. b 4. d 5. c 6. b 7. a 8. a 9. c 10. b

NOTES

22 UPPER ALIMENTARY SYSTEM INFECTIONS

The upper alimentary tract includes the organs from the mouth down to the stomach along with accessory structures such as the salivary glands. Much of the alimentary tract itself has an associated normal flora and represents one of the major routes of entry into the body by pathogens and opportunists. Our food and water contain a large variety of organisms that find their way into the body by this route. The stomach with its acid contents is an extremely efficient barrier to many microorganisms reaching the lower alimentary tract. The stomach was considered not too many years ago as being essentially sterile and not a usual site of infection. Infection of the stomach is now known to be commonplace.

KEY CONCEPTS

1. The alimentary tract is a major route for the entry of pathogenic microorganisms into the body.
2. The pathogenesis of tooth decay depends on both diet and acid forming bacteria, which are adapted to colonize hard, smooth surfaces within the mouth.
3. Infections of the esophagus are so unusual in normal people that their occurrence suggests immunodeficiency.
4. A properly functioning stomach destroys most microorganisms before they reach the intestine.

SUMMARY

I. Anatomy and Physiology
   A. The upper alimentary system is composed of the mouth and salivary glands, esophagus, and stomach.
   B. Degradation of complex foods begins in the mouth with the grinding action of teeth and mixing with saliva. Saliva is produced by glands in the floor of the mouth and on the sides of the face. It contains the enzyme amylase that begins the degradation of starch. It protects the teeth by several mechanisms.
   C. Three different kinds of cells line the stomach. One produces hydrochloric acid; another, enzymes; and the third, mucus. One of the important stomach enzymes is pepsin, which begins the degradation of proteins under acid conditions.

II. Normal Flora
   A. The species of bacteria that inhabit the mouth colonize different locations depending on their ability to attach to structures such as the tongue, cheeks, teeth, or other bacteria.
   B. Dental plaque consists of enormous quantities of bacteria of various species attached to teeth or to each other. Streptococci and actinomycetes are generally responsible for the initiation of plaque formation.
   C. The presence of teeth allows for colonization by anaerobic bacteria.

III. Infections Caused by Oral Bacteria
   A. Dental caries is an infectious disease caused mainly by *Streptococcus mutans* and related species.
   B. Pathogenesis of cariogenic dental plaque involves formation by *S. mutans* of extracellular glucans from dietary sucrose.
   C. Penetration of the calcium phosphate tooth structure depends on acid production by cariogenic dental plaque. Prolonged acid production is fostered by the ability of *S. mutans* to form intracellular polysaccharide.
   D. Control of dental caries depends mainly on supplying adequate fluoride and restricting dietary sucrose. Dental sealants are important in children.
   E. Periodontal disease is mainly responsible for tooth loss in older people.
   F. Endocarditis in patients with abnormal heart valves is commonly due to oral bacteria. Entry of these bacteria into the blood stream frequently occurs with dental procedures.

IV. Viral Diseases of the Mouth and Salivary Glands
  A. Herpes simplex is caused by an enveloped DNA virus that can be readily cultivated in tissue cell cultures. Infected cells show intranuclear inclusion bodies.
  B. Latent infections are characteristic of herpesviruses. HSV persists inside sensory nerves in a non-infectious form that can become infectious and produce active disease when the body undergoes certain stresses.
  C. Mumps is caused by an enveloped RNA virus that is prone to infect the parotid glands, meninges, testicles, and other body tissues.
  D. Mumps virus generally causes more severe disease in persons beyond the age of puberty.
  E. Mumps can be prevented using a live vaccine.

V. Infections of the Esophagus and Stomach
  A. Esophageal infections are seen mainly in immunocompromised individuals. The main causes are herpes simplex virus and the yeast, *Candida albicans.*
  B. *Helicobacter pylori* gastritis is a common infectious disease of the stomach.
    1. *H. pylori* predisposes the stomach and upper duodenum to peptic ulcers.
    2. Treatment is difficult even though the organism is susceptible to antimicrobial medications *in vitro*. However, effective treatment prevents peptic ulcer recurrence.

TERMS AND DEFINITIONS

1. The name for calcified plaque on the teeth is _____ .

2. _____ is a substance in saliva that binds to iron and removes it from use by bacteria.

3. A low _____ potential means that little or no oxygen is available for growth of bacteria.

4. _____ is the inspection of an internal area of the body with the use of a flexible fiberoptic instrument.

5. Insoluble polysaccharides composed of repeating subunits of glucose are called_____ .

6. The _____ is a muscular valve that determines the rate at which the stomach contents enter the intestine.

7. Masses of bacteria attached to the teeth by various polymeric substances are called _____ .

8. _____ is a painful finger infection caused by Herpes simplex virus and an occupational hazard among dentists.

9. _____ is a chronic inflammatory process involving the tissues around the roots of the teeth.

10. An inflammation of the gums is called _____ .

SELF-TEST OF READING MATERIAL

1. The teeth are made up largely of
  a. urease.
  b. hydroxyapatite crystals.
  c. enamel.
  d. dentin.
  e. amylase.

2. Herpes simplex virus can remain latent in a non-infectious form within
    a. the lips.
    b. the mouth.
    c. saliva.
    d. sensory nerves.
    e. plaque.

3. *Helicobacter pylori* infection can be diagnosed from the presence of which of the following in stomach biopsy?
    a. amylase
    b. intranuclear inclusions
    c. urease
    d. hydroxyapatite
    e. acid

4. Which of the following is commonly associated with recurrences of herpes simplex virus?
    a. fever
    b. sunburn
    c. menstruation
    d. All of the above are associated with recurrences.
    e. Only a and b are associated with recurrences.

5. Sterility is common in older men in which the mumps have "dropped" and infected the testicles.
    a. True
    b. False

6. Which of the following is associated with an increased incidence of stomach cancer?
    a. herpes simplex virus
    b. mumps
    c. halitosis
    d. *Helicobacter pylori*
    e. herpetic whitlow

7. Ancyclovir does not effect latent herpes simplex virus so it does not cure the disease but it can relieve the symptoms and decrease the amount of virus being shed.
    a. True
    b. False

8. The severe swelling and pain associated with mumps is due to
    a. endotoxins.
    b. inflammatory response.
    c. immune complexes.
    d. exotoxins.
    e. Two of the above are correct.

9. Mumps initially reproduces in the
    a. blood system.
    b. nervous system.
    c. salivary glands.
    d. digestive system.
    e. respiratory system.

10. Mumps vaccine is recommended for those infected with HIV because the benefit far outweighs the risk from the vaccine.
    a. True
    b. False

REVIEW QUESTIONS

1. Why is penicillin started only a few hours before a dental procedure on someone that has known abnormal heart valves?

2. Since only one serotype of mumps virus is known, that makes it a good candidate for eradication. Explain.

3. Why must teeth be present in order for anaerobes to colonize the mouth?

4. Describe how mumps virus results in swelling of the salivary glands?

23 *LOWER ALIMENTARY SYSTEM INFECTIONS*

Gastrointestinal infections of the lower alimentary tract are among the most common and often most severe infections of humans. The stomach protects against a large number of pathogens, but many have adapted means to get through the stomach unharmed. Many parasites, such as worms and protozoa, even use the acid condition of the stomach to initiate their exit from protective cysts and eggs. Diseases of the lower alimentary tract are usually transmitted by the fecal-oral route meaning that the next host gets the disease from eating food or drinking water, or putting contaminated items such as fingers into their mouth. The lower bowel is home to a variety of bacteria belonging to the normal flora. Diarrhea, from simple to invasive forms, is responsible for millions of deaths worldwide each year.

KEY CONCEPTS

1. Some microbial toxins alter the secretory function of cells in the small intestine without killing or visibly damaging them.
2. Unsuspected human carriers can remain sources of enteric infections for many years.
3. Viruses, bacteria, and protozoa are important causes of human intestinal diseases.
4. Food poisoning may be caused either by infectious microorganisms consumed with the food or toxic products of microbial growth in food.

SUMMARY

I. Anatomy and Physiology of the Lower Alimentary System
   A. Important functions include breakdown of food macromolecules to their subunits, absorbing nutrients, and recycling fluids.
   B. Bile, produced by the liver, is inhibitory for many bacteria, and aids digestion of fats and vitamins. It causes the brown color of feces when acted on by intestinal bacteria.
   C. The pancreas produces insulin and alkaline fluid containing digestive enzymes.
   D. The small intestine secretes digestive juices and absorbs nutrients. It has a large surface area.
   E. The large intestine contains large numbers of microorganisms, many of which are opportunistic pathogens. It helps recycle body water.

II. Normal Flora of the Digestive Tract
   A. The small intestine has few microorganisms.
   B. Microorganisms make up about one-third of the weight of feces.
   C. Anaerobes of the genera *Lactobacillus* and *Bacteroides* are the most prevalent.
   D. The biochemical activities of microorganisms in the digestive tract include synthesis of vitamins, degradation of indigestible substances, competitive inhibition of pathogens, production of cholesterol, chemical alteration of medications, and carcinogen production.

III. Bacterial Disease of the Digestive Tract
   A. Diarrhea is a major cause of death worldwide.
   B. Cholera is a severe form of diarrhea caused by a toxin of *Vibrio cholerae* that acts on the epithelium of the small intestine.
   C. Species of *Shigella* are common causes of dysentery because they invade the colon epithelium.
   D. Gastroenteritis is often caused by salmonellae of animal origin. The organisms often enter the intestinal tract with food, usually eggs and poultry.
   E. Gastroenteritis can be caused by certain strains *Escherichia coli*. Only strains possessing virulence factors cause disease. These factors often depend on plasmids. Plasmids, and therefore virulence, can be transferred to other enteric organisms.

F. *Campylobacter jejuni* is a common bacterial cause of diarrhea in the United States. Like the salmonellae, it usually originates from domestic animals. Like the shigellae and certain strains of *E. coli* it can cause dysentery.

G. Typhoid fever is caused by *Salmonella typhi.*
   1. The disease is characterized by high fever, headache, and abdominal pain. Untreated, it has a high mortality rate.
   2. Human carriers maintain the disease.
   3. A new oral attenuated vaccine helps in prevention.

H. Food Poisoning
   1. Illness caused by toxic products of microbial growth in food.
   2. Staphylococcal food poisoning, caused by certain strains of *Staphylococcus aureus,* is one of the most common forms. The toxin is heat stable.
   3. Food poisoning is also caused by the spore-forming, Gram-positive rods, *Clostridium perfringens* and *Bacillus cereus.*
   4. Botulism is characterized by paralysis and occurs in three forms: food-borne, intestinal, and wound.

IV. Poisoning Caused by Fungi
   A. Growth of certain species of fungi on grain can cause ergot poisoning.
   B. Aflatoxins are fungal poisons produced by molds of the genus *Aspergillus.* Liver damage and certain cancers can result from ingestion of aflatoxins.

V. Viral Infections of the Lower Alimentary System
   A. Viral Hepatitis.
      1. Hepatitis A virus (HAV) is spread by fecal contamination of hands, food, or water. Most cases are mild and may even be asymptomatic. Antibody to the virus is widespread in the population.
      2. Hepatitis B virus (HBV) is spread mainly by blood and blood products, but also by sexual intercourse, and from mother to infant. HBV is generally more severe than HAV. Chronic infection is fairly frequent and can lead to scarring of the liver and liver cancer. Carriers are common and can have infectious virus in their bloodstreams for years without knowing it.
      3. Other hepatitis viruses
         a. Hepatitis C virus (HCV) causes most of the cases of transfusion-associated hepatitis.
         b. Hepatitis delta virus (HDV) is a defective RNA virus that requires the presence of HBV to replicate.
         c. Hepatitis E virus (HEV), an RNA virus, is transmitted by the fecal-oral route and can cause fatalities, especially in pregnant women.
   B. Viral gastroenteritis.
      1. Rotoviruses and Norwalk viruses are the most important causes of this disease. Rotoviruses affect mainly children, but also can cause traveler's diarrhea. Norwalk viruses cause about half of the United States gastroenteritis outbreaks.

VI. Protozoan Diseases of the Lower Alimentary System
   A. Giardiasis is caused by *Giardia lamblia* and is usually transmitted by drinking water contaminated by feces of humans and wild animals. It is distributed worldwide and is a common cause of traveler's diarrhea.
   B. *Entamoeba histolytica* is an important cause of dysentery. Amebiasis is often chronic, and infection can spread to the liver and other organs.

TERMS AND DEFINITIONS

1. The inside surface of the intestine is covered with many finger-like projections called _____ .

2. _____ are specialized surface structures on many pathogens that allow them to adhere to the intestinal epithelial cells.

3. The enterotoxin produced by *Shigella dysenteriae* that causes abscesses and ulcerations of the intestinal tract is known as _____ toxin.

4. _____ is a yellow color of the skin and eyes caused by bile pigments.

5. The presence of viruses in the blood is called _____ .

6. _____ is the living as a parasite on or in a host.

7. The enterotoxin produced by *Vibrio cholerae* is called _____ .

8. Bloody, pus-filled diarrhea is known as _____ .

9. Substances in the bile called _____ act as detergents and help _____ fats in the intestine.

10. _____ are collections of lymphoid cells in the intestinal wall that are susceptible to invasion by *Salmonella typhi*.

SELF-TEST OF READING MATERIAL

Match the list of causative agents on the right with the description of the food poisoning on the left.

_____ 1. Ergot poisoning resulting from eating bread prepared from grain with fungal growth

_____ 2. Toxin produced during sporulation

_____ 3. Most severe type of food poisoning following ingestion of preformed toxin

_____ 4. Most common type of food poisoning with a heat-stable enterotoxin

_____ 5. Mild type of food poisoning associated with rice dishes

_____ 6. Acute poisoning capable of producing liver damage and possibly liver cancer

a. *Staphylococcus aureus*
b. *Clostridium perfringens*
c. *Bacillus cereus*
d. *Clostridium botulinum*
e. *Claviceps purpurea*
f. *Aspergillus*

7. Botulinum toxin, which causes a fatal food poisoning, is
   1. heat labile.
   2. an enterotoxin.
   3. heat stable.

   4. a protein.
   5. a neurotoxin.
   6. a lipopolysaccharide.

   a. 2,3,6
   b. 1,4,5
   c. 1,2,6

   d. 3,4,5
   e. 1,2,4

8. Infant or intestinal botulism is different from botulism food poisoning because
   a. a neurotoxin is not involved.
   b. infant botulism is due to an organism and not a toxin.
   c. infant botulism results from an infection.
   d. botulism food poisoning is due to an enterotoxin.
   e. it is carried by honey.

9. In the United States, the most common source of botulism is
   a. eclairs.
   b. home canned foods.
   c. fish.

   d. sausages.
   e. water.

10. The recent epidemic of intestinal disease associated with *E. coli* strain O157:H7 was caused by
    a. enterotoxigenic *E. coli*
    b. enterohemorrhagic *E. coli*
    c. enteropathogenic *E. coli*

    d. enteroaggregative *E. coli*
    e. enteroinvasive *E. coli*

11. Pet turtles have been shown to be an important source of
    a. *Salmonella.*
    b. *Clostridium botulinum.*
    c. *Giardia lamblia.*

    d. enterohemorrhagic *E. coli.*
    e. *Shigella dysenteriae.*

12. The most common cause of cases of post-transfusion hepatitis is
    a. hepatitis A virus.
    b. hepatitis B virus.
    c. hepatitis C virus.

    d. a and b are correct.
    e. All three occur with equal frequency.

13. Which of the following is responsible for most of the water-borne disease epidemics in the United States in which a cause is identified?
    a. hepatitis A virus
    b. enterotoxigenic *E. coli*
    c. *Shigella dysenteriae*

    d. *Salmonella*
    e. *Giardia lamblia*

14. Suppression of the normal flora of the intestine with antibiotics increases susceptibility to
    a. *Clostridium difficile*
    b. *Salmonella enteritidis*
    c. *Entamoeba histolytica*

    d. a and b are correct.
    e. None of the above.

15. Giardiasis, sometimes called "beaver fever" or "backpacker's disease," was thought to be associated exclusively with drinking water in mountain streams, but is now also found in day care centers associated with diaper changing.
    a. True
    b. False

REVIEW QUESTIONS

1. Various strains of *E. coli* mimic other intestinal infections. List the four main types of virulent strains of *E. coli* along with the disease or organism that each mimics.

2. Compare and contrast the food poisoning toxins of *Staphylococcus aureus* and *Clostridium botulinum*.

3. Why is bile included in some selective microbiological media?

4. What are adhesions and why are they important to intestinal pathogens?

5. What is significant about the infective stages of *Entamoeba histolytica* and *Giardia lamblia*?

6. How do hepatitis A and hepatitis B differ in their transmission?

ANSWERS:
  Terms and Definitions
    1. villi 2. adhesions 3. Shiga toxin 4. jaundice 5. viremia 6. infestation 7. cholergen 8. dysentery
    9. bile salts/emulsify 10. Peyer's patches
  Self-Test of Reading Material
    1. e 2. b 3. d 4. a 5. c 6. f 7. b 8. c 9. b 10. b 11. a 12. c 13. e 14. d 15. a

24 GENITOURINARY INFECTIONS

Genitourinary tract infections are caused by a number of opportunists that are part of the normal flora of the body or by pathogens introduced from the outside. While many of the infections are considered sexually transmitted diseases, most of the remaining infections occur when there is some breakdown in the barriers that protect the genitourinary tract. In the urinary tract this includes conditions that interfere with the normal flow of urine. Interference with the normal flora in the vagina is a significant first step to the establishment of an infection. Women are also more susceptible to urinary tract infections because of a short urethra and the proximity to the intestinal tract.

KEY CONCEPTS

1. The flushing action of urination is a key defense mechanism against bladder infections.
2. During the childbearing years, a woman's hormones are important in the vagina's resistance to infection because estrogen influences the vagina's normal flora.
3. Transmission of genital tract infections usually resuires direct human-to-human contact.
4. Unsuspected sexually transmitted infections of pregnant mothers pose a serious threat to fetuses and newborn babies.
5. Asymptomatic infections can cause serious genital tract damage and are transmissible to other people.

SUMMARY

I. Anatomy and Physiology
   A. The main structures of the urinary tract—the kidneys, bladder, ureters, and urethra—are generally well protected from infection.
   B. Urinary tract infections occur more frequently in women than in men because of the shortness of the female urethra and its closeness to the genital and intestinal tracts.
   C. The vagina is the site of entry for a number of infections.

II. Normal Flora of the Genitourinary Tract
   A. In women, the normal flora is dependent on the action of estrogen hormones that promote the deposition of glycogen in cells lining the vagina. Lactobacilli normally help prevent colonization by pathogens.

III. Urinary Tract Infections
   A. Bladder infections occur when frequent, complete emptying fails to take place. This allows accumulation of urine, a nutritional medium for many bacteria, and permits multiplication of pathogenic bacteria that are present.
   B. Kidney infection may complicate untreated bladder infection when pathogens ascend the ureters and involve the kidneys.
   C. Ninety percent of urinary tract infections are caused by enterobacteria from the person's own normal intestinal flora.
   D. *Escherichia coli* is the cause of the majority of urinary tract infections in otherwise healthy women.
   E. *Pseudomonas aeruginosa* infections are difficult to treat because these bacteria are generally resistant to many antibiotics.
   F. Proper collection and culturing of urine specimens is critically important in identifying the cause of urinary infections because during urination, bacteria are introduced into the specimen from the lower urethra and vagina.
   G. Causative organisms of diseases involving areas of the body other than the urinary tract may be found in urine.

IV. Genital Tract Infections
A. Bacterial sexually transmitted diseases.
1. Gonorrhea, caused by *Neisseria gonorrhoeae*, is among the most prevalent venereal diseases. Ophthalmia neonatorum, a very destructive eye disease of the newborn can be acquired during passage through birth canal in a mother infected with *N. gonorrhoeae*. Infections in men may extend to the prostate gland and testes. In women, infection can spread upward through the uterus and into the fallopian tubes resulting in pelvic inflammatory disease. This can produce scar tissue formation and cause the blockage of ova passing through the fallopian tubes. This condition can cause sterility or ectopic pregnancy.
2. Syphilis, caused by *Treponema pallidum*, can imitate many other diseases during its progression. An infected asymptomatic pregnant woman can transmit the organism to her fetus.
3. Symptoms and complications of chlamydia infections are very similar to those of gonorrhea. Asymptomatic carriers are common.
4. Chancroid is caused by *Haemophilus ducreyi*, an X-factor requiring bacterium, and in some tropical countries is second only to gonorrhea among the sexually transmitted diseases. Like other ulcerative STD's, it can increase the risk of acquiring HIV infection.
B. Viral sexually transmitted diseases.
1. Genital herpes simplex, caused by herpes simplex virus type 2, is among the most common venereal diseases. Recurrences are common. The viral chromosome exists within nerve cells during asymptomatic times. The disease can be transmitted during symptom-free intervals. It is incurable, but can be suppressed by medication.
2. Genital warts are caused by human papillomaviruses. Some strains are strongly associated with cervical cancer. The warts can be removed, but there is no cure of the infection.
3. HIV infection is currently pandemic and probably fatal in all cases. No vaccine or medical cure is available, but the spread of the infection can be halted by applying current knowledge and practices.
C. Other genital tract infections.
1. Bacterial vaginosis is the most common cause of vaginal symptoms. It is characterized by a decrease in lactobacilli and an increase in *Gardnerella vaginalis* and anaerobic bacteria.
2. Yeast vulvovaginitis is caused by *Candida albicans,* commonly a normal part of the vaginal flora. This organism becomes pathogenic when the normal bacterial flora is reduced by antibiotic treatment.
3. Vaginitis can be caused by the protozoan *Trichomonas vaginalis.* Infections in men are usually asymptomatic.
4. Puerperal fever can be caused by *Streptococcus pyogenes* or anaerobic bacteria. Contaminated instruments or hands spread the disease.
5. Toxic shock syndrome is caused by the growth of certain strains of *Staphylococcus aureus* . This condition may occur in the vagina after high-absorbency tampons have been left in place too long.

SELF-TEST OF READING MATERIAL

Use the following list of organisms to match the description or name of an infection below.

a. *Haemophilus ducreyi*
b. herpes simplex virus type 2
c. *Trichomonas vaginalis*
d. *Staphylococcus aureus*
e. *Leptospira*
f. *Treponema pallidum*
g. *Neisseria gonorrhoeae*
h. *Pseudomonas aeruginosa*

i. *Candida albicans*
j. human papilloma virus
k. *Chlamydia trachomatis*
l. *Streptococcus faecalis*
m. human immunodeficiency virus
n. *Escherichia coli*
o. herpes simplex virus type 1

_____ 1. Chancroid

_____ 2. Toxic shock syndrome

_____ 3. Genital warts

_____ 4. 90% of urinary tract infections in healthy individuals

_____ 5. Disseminated gonococcal disease

_____ 6. An organism that causes urinary tract infections and is very resistant to antibiotics

_____ 7. Vaginal organism usually kept under control by the normal flora

_____ 8. The "great imitator" disease

_____ 9. Hard chancre

_____ 10. The agent of AIDS

_____ 11. Protozoan infection of women that is usually asymptomatic in men

_____ 12. Treatment for gonorrhea now assumes this organism is also present

_____ 13. The most common Gram-positive agent in urinary tract infections

_____ 14. Disease can be transmitted in urine-contaminated water

_____ 15. The "pale thread"

_____ 16. Associated with cancer of the cervix

_____ 17. Infection that mimics gonorrhea

_____ 18. Causes ophthalmia neonatorum

_____ 19. Pelvic inflammatory disease

_____ 20. Causes scarring of fallopian tubes that can lead to ectopic pregnancy

21. The hard chancre of primary syphilis is due to
    a. exotoxins.
    b. inflammatory reaction.
    c. immune complexes.
    d. endotoxins.
    e. Two of the above are correct.

22. Which of the following has a normal resident flora?
    a. lower urethra
    b. upper ureter
    c. kidney
    d. upper urethra
    e. lower ureter

23. The urinary tract is protected from infection by
    a. downward flow of urine.
    b. antimicrobial organic acids in urine.
    c. antibodies in the urine.
    d. All of the above are correct.
    e. Only a and b are correct.

24. The symptoms of secondary syphilis are
    a. due to the presence of large numbers of bacteria.
    b. due to endotoxins.
    c. due to exotoxins.
    d. associated with concurrent gonococcal infections.
    e. due to immune complexes.

25. Genital herpes can be caused by either herpes simplex virus type 1 or type 2, but infections by type 2 virus produces more severe lesions with a greater frequency of recurrence.
    a. True
    b. False

26. *Trichomonas vaginalis* does not have
    a. mitochondria.
    b. a cyst stage.
    c. flagella.
    d. a and b are correct.
    e. a and c are correct.

27. A non-treponemal test for syphilis detects the presence of
    a. treponemal antigens in serum.
    b. beef heart lipids in serum.
    c. antibody-like proteins in serum.
    d. beef heart antibodies in serum.
    e. viable *Treponema pallidum*.

28. Gonorrhea in men is usually asymptomatic and resolves itself with treatment.
    a. True
    b. False

29. Erythromycin is replacing silver nitrate in the prophylaxis of opthalmia neonatorum because silver nitrate is not effective against _____, which also often occurs in combination with gonococcal infections.
    a. *Chlamydia trachomatis*
    b. *Candida albicans*
    e. HIV
    d. *Trichomonas vaginalis*
    e. *Treponema pallidum*

30. Genital warts can be removed with laser treatment or freezing with liquid nitrogen, but this does not cure the infection.
    a. True
    b. False

REVIEW QUESTIONS

1. List the seven symptoms that should alert one to the possibility of a sexually transmitted disease.

2. Describe a non-treponemal test for syphilis and a test that uses treponemal antigen.

3. What is the relation of estrogen to resistance of the vagina to infection?

4. Why are hospital patients and women more likely to contract a urinary tract infection?

5. Describe the characteristics of the three stages of syphilis?

6. What can account for the recent rapid increase in the number of cases of congenital syphilis.

NOTES

25 *NERVOUS SYSTEM INFECTIONS*

For fairly obvious reasons, infections of the nervous system, especially the central nervous system, are extremely serious. The nervous system does not have any normal flora associated with it. Infectious agents must enter across the blood-brain barrier, by way of the peripheral nerves, or by direct extension from wounds or infections of associated areas such as mastoids, ears or sinuses. Treatment of nervous system infections is often difficult because most drugs or antibiotics will not cross the blood-brain barrier. Representatives of the bacteria, viruses, protozoa, and the fungi, nevertheless, manage to establish and produce disease in the nervous system.

KEY CONCEPTS

1. Infectious diseases of the central nervous system are uncommon compared to infections elsewhere in the body because pathogens usually cannot cross the blood-brain barrier.
2. The presence or absence of receptors on the surface of different kinds of nervous system cells determines their susceptibility to infection and thus the symptoms of an infectious disease.
3. The nervous system is infected primarily from the blood stream, via the nerve cells or through cranial bone.
4. Antimicrobial medicines are effective in central nervous system infections only if they are able to cross the blood-brain barrier.

SUMMARY

I. Anatomy and Physiology
   A. The brain and spinal cord make up the nervous system.
   B. There are two kinds of nerves.
      1. Motor neurons cause parts of body to act.
      2. Sensory neurons transmit sensations such as heat, pain, touch, light, and sound.
   C. Cerebrospinal fluid (CSF) is produced in cavities inside brain and flows out over the brain, spinal cord, and nerves. Samples can be removed and tested for cause of central nervous system infections.
   D. Meninges are the three membranes that cover the surface of the brain and spinal cord. Cerebrospinal fluid flows between the two innermost membranes.
   E. Infectious organisms can reach the brain and spinal cord in three ways.
      1. The bloodstream where the blood-brain barrier acts as protection.
      2. The nerves.
      3. Direct extension through the skull by infections elsewhere, such as from the middle ear or sinuses.

II. Leading Causes of Bacterial Infections of the Nervous System
   A. *Neisseria meningitidis*, the cause of meningococcal meningitis, is a Gram-negative diplococcus. Release of endotoxin from the organism can cause shock and death. *N. meningitidis* is capable of causing epidemics.
   B. *Haemophilus influenzae*, a leading cause of bacterial meningitis, is a tiny Gram-negative, coccobacillus that requires X- and V- factors for growth. It produces satellites in culture. Some strains have acquired a plasmid that codes for penicillinase.
   C. *Streptococcus pneumoniae*, the cause of pneumococcal meningitis is a Gram-positive, encapsulated diplococcus. Pneumonia and ear or sinus infection often accompanies meningitis. *S. pneumoniae* is the most common cause of meningitis in adults.
   D. *Escherichia coli*, an enteric, Gram-negative rod, is one of leading causes of meningitis in newborns.
   E. *Streptococcus agalactiae*, another leading cause of meningitis of newborns, has a Lancefield Group B cell wall polysaccharide.
   F. *Listeria monocytogenes*, a motile, aerobic, Gram-positive rod, causes meningitis in newborns and people with other diseases.

G. Hansen's disease (leprosy) is characterized by the invasion of peripheral nerves by the acid-fast bacillus, *Mycobacterium leprae*. This organism has not yet been cultivated *in vitro*. Hansen's disease occurs in two main forms, tuberculoid and lepromatous, depending on the immune status of the individual.

III. Viral Diseases of the Nervous System
    A. Sporadic encephalitis—herpes simplex virus is the most important cause.
    B. Epidemic enecphalitis—usually caused by arboviruses.
        1. La Crosse encephalitis virus—maintained in *Aedes* mosquitoes and rodents.
        2. St. Louis encephalitis virus—maintained in *Culex* mosquitoes and birds.
    C. Poliomyelitis, which involves the motor nerve cells of the brain and spinal cord, is caused by three picornaviruses, polioviruses 1, 2, and 3.
        1. Motor nerve destruction leads to paralysis, muscle wasting, and failure of normal bone development.
        2. Post-polio syndrome occurs years after poliomyelitis and is probably caused by the death of nerve cells that had compensated for ones killed by the poliovirus.
    D. Rabies is transmitted mainly through the bite of an infected animal.
        1. The incubation period is long, often measured in months and sometimes years.
        2. The virus multiplies in muscle and then travels through nerve cells to the brain. After multiplying in the brain, it spreads outward, through the nerves, to infect other body tissues, rapidly causing death.

IV. Fungal Central Nervous System Diseases
    A. Cryptococcal meningoencephalitis is an infection of the meninges and brain caused by *Filobasidiella (Cryptococcus) neoformans*. Infection originates in the lung after inhaling dust laden with the fungi. The organism is often associated with pigeon droppings. This disease is a common, serious complication of AIDS.

V. Protozoan Central Nervous System Diseases
    A. African Sleeping Sickness is caused by *Trypanosoma brucei*.
        1. During infection, the organism shows bursts of growth, each appearing with different surface proteins.
        2. Each of these variants requires that the body respond with a new antibody since the prior one is ineffectual.

TERMS AND DEFINITIONS

1. A state in which there is insufficient blood pressure to supply adequate flow of blood to vital organs

   is called _____ .

2. _____ are long, thin extensions of nerve cells that transmit electrical impulses.

3. A clear fluid filling the ventricles of the brain and covering the brain and the spinal cord is called

   the _____ fluid.

4. Characteristic inclusion bodies at the site of rabies virus replication in brain cells are

   are called _____ bodies.

5. _____ is an inflammation of the meninges.

6. Hypersensitivity to sera such as horse serum used in rabies treatment is called _____ .

7. _____ literally means "fear of water," but is a painful spasm of the throat and respiratory muscles provoked by swallowing or seeing liquids.

8. Three membranes that cover the the surface of the brain and the spinal cord are called the _____ .

9. _____ are purplish spots resulting from small hemorrages under the skin and are a

classical sign of _____ .

10. A _____ vaccine is one in which antigenic determinants are covalently linked to another protein for improved immune response.

SELF-TEST OF READING MATERIAL

1. People with tuberculoid leprosy, the least severe form of leprosy, rarely transmit the disease to others.
   a. True
   b. False

2. Which of the following is true about the normal flora of the nervous system?
   a. Only transient organisms are present.
   b. Microorganisms are present only in portions of the central nervous system.
   c. The nervous system does not have a normal flora.
   d. Microorganisms are present only in portions of the peripheral nervous system.
   e. a and c are correct.

3. Infections of the central nervous system and brain are difficult to treat because
   a. drugs cannot pass through the blood-brain barrier.
   b. nerve tissue does not regenerate so that healing is very difficult.
   c. most infections are caused by fungi and they are difficult to treat.
   d. drugs also affect the brain and cause damage.
   e. most infections occur only after extensive brain damage.

4. In rabies infections
   a. treatment after infection is possible now because of new viral vaccines.
   b. most cases in the United States today are in wild animals and not dogs.
   c. the incubation period is often long and dependent on the site of the bite and the dose of virus.
   d. a and b are correct.
   e. b and c are correct.

Use the list on the right, which describes means of disease transmission, to match the appropriate infection on the left.

_____ 5. poliomyelitis

_____ 6. arbovirus encephalitis

_____ 7. *E. coli* meningitis

_____ 8. pneumococcal meningitis

_____ 9. leprosy

_____ 10. *Listeria* meningitis

_____ 11. cryptococcal meningitis

_____ 12. African sleeping sickness

_____ 13. meningococcal meningitis

_____ 14. rabies

a. inhalation of infectious droplets
b. tsetse fly bite
c. infection in birth canal
d. inhalation of dust particles
e. ingestion of dairy products
f. animal bite
g. direct contact
h. fecal-oral route
i. mosquito bite

15. Hansen's disease, or leprosy, is best chacterized as
    a. a highly contagious disease.
    b. an infection of the perphrial nervous system.
    c. an acute infection.
    d. an infection of the central nervous system.
    e. Two of the above are correct.

16. *Streptococcus pneumoniae, Hemophilius influenzae,* and *Neisseria meningitidis* seldom cause meningitis in newborns because
    a. most mothers have antibodies against them and these are tranferred across the placenta.
    b. newborns lack the appropriate adhesions for the infections.
    c. most mothers have antigens against them and these are tranferred across the placenta.
    d. these organisms lack the appropriate adhesions for the infections.
    e. The statement is false because these organisms do often cause meningitis in newborns.

17. Sentinel chickens are useful in detecting the presence of diseases transmitted by
    a. animal bites.
    b. mosquito bites.
    c. direct contact.
    d. chickens.
    e. aerosol droplet.

18. Rabies can be transferred by corneal transplant.
    a. True
    b. False

19. The causative agent of spongiform encephalopathies appears to be
    a. a virus.
    b. an unusual protein.
    c. common in humans.
    d. a protozoan.
    e. easily cured.

20. Poliomyelitis is actually an infection of the digestive tract that spreads to the nervous system in a small percentage of infected individuals.
    a. True
    b. False

REVIEW QUESTIONS

1. Why is it not a good idea, disease-wise, to squeeze a pimple at the corner of your mouth?

2. Explain how the Shwartzman phenomenon relates to the rapidly fatal outcome of some infections by *Neisseria meningitidis.*

3. Describe how *Naegleria fowleri* gets into the central nervous system and from where.

4. Complete the following table by listing the principal species of bacteria that cause meningitis at the different ages.

AGE GROUP	PRINCIPLE SPECIES THAT CAUSE BACTERIAL MENINGITIS
Newborns	
Children	
Adults	

NOTES

26 *WOUND INFECTIONS*

A wound or break in the skin surface can permit any number of different pathogens or opportunists to enter the body and initiate colonization, infection, and disease. These wounds may be as minor as a friendly scratch from your favorite kitty to as major as someone getting an arm or leg caught in a piece of farm equipment. They all have one important consequence in common; bacteria and fungi can cross our first line of defense against disease. Tetanus results from an organism that remains at the site of infection but causes its destruction with a powerful nerve exotoxin. At the other extreme is gas gangrene that is highly invasive because the organism extends from damaged wound tissue into healthy tissue. This chapter details the major aspects of such infections.

KEY CONCEPTS

1. Bacteria with little invasive ability can produce serious disease if they synthesize toxins that are absorbed and carried to other parts of the body.
2. Since a wide variety of pathogens infect wounds, widely differing diagnostic and treatment methods may be required.
3. *Staphylococcus aureus* is the most important cause of wound infections because it is commonly carried by humans.
4. Bacterial exotoxins from different species of bacteria may have the same mode of action but cause distinctly different diseases because the toxin molecules enter different body cells.
5. The prevalence of certain wound infections is determined by factors such as geography and occupation.
6. Bacteria with little invasive ability when growing alone can invade tissue when growing with other bacteria.

SUMMARY

I. Features of Wounds
   A. Wound abscesses are localized collections of pus. They lack blood vessels and inflammation surrounds the abscess. The microorganisms present may not be actively growing and therefore not affected by antibiotics. Microorganisms in abscesses are potential sources of infection elsewhere in the body.
   B. Anaerobic conditions in wounds permit the growth of anaerobic pathogens. Puncture wounds, dirty wounds, and those with dead tissue are likely to be anaerobic.
   C. Even microorganisms usually considered harmless can cause serious infections if the tissue is crushed or the host is immunodeficient.

II. Bacterial Infections of Wounds
   A. *Staphylococcus aureus* (coagulase-positive staphylococcus) is the most common cause of infections in surgical wounds.
   B. *Pseudomonas aeruginosa* is a common cause of burn infections. *P. aeruginosa* is usually resistant to most antibiotics.
   C. Clostridial wound infections.
      1. Tetanus (lockjaw) is caused by a toxin produced by *Clostridium tetani*. Colonization, even of minor wounds, by *C. tetani* can result in tetanus. The disease is often fatal, but can be prevented by proper immunization and care of all wounds.
      2. Gas gangrene is marked by necrosis of muscle tissue. It is most commonly caused by the anaerobe *Clostridium perfringens*.
   D. Nonclostridial anaerobic infections of wounds.
      1. The primary causative agents are *Bacteroides*, *Fusobacterium*, and *Peptostreptococcus*.
      2. Actinomycosis is caused by *Actinomyces israelii*, which is considered normal flora of the human mouth and intestinal tract. Infections can originate from dental and intestinal surgery.

  E. Bite wounds.
    1. Infection of bite wounds may result from a single species of bacterium or from multiple species acting synergistically.
    2. *Pasteurella multocida* infection commonly complicates animal bite wounds.
    3. Cat scratch disease is characterized by localized skin papules, followed by large and often, pus-filled lymph nodes .
    4. Rat bite fever can be caused by either *Spirillum minus* or *Streptobacillus moniliformis. S. minus* cannot be cultivated *in vitro,* while *S. moniliformis* characteristically has cell wall deficient variants called L-forms.
    5. Human bites often result in severe synergistic infections. Prompt treatment is important.

III. Fungal Infections of Wounds
  A. Sporotrichosis is a chronic fungal disease mainly of those who work with vegetation. The causative agent is *Sporothrix schenckii,* usually introduced into wounds caused by thorns and splinters.

SELF-TEST OF READING MATERIAL

Match the organism on the right with its description on the left.

_____ 1. The major cause of death in burn patients

_____ 2. The major cause of surgical wound infections

_____ 3. Organism spreads to healthy tissue with alpha toxin

_____ 4. Introduced into wounds by thorns and splinters

_____ 5. Produces a greenish discoloration of wound

_____ 6. A non-invasive exotoxin producer

_____ 7. The most common cause of burn infections

_____ 8. Produce "sulfur granules" in wounds

_____ 9. Causes cat scratch fever

_____ 10. Hospital environment is source for patient

_____ 11. Most common cause of myonecrosis

_____ 12. Newly recognized causes of wound infections

_____ 13. Most difficult burn infection to treat

_____ 14. Hyperbaric oxygen treatment sometimes helpful

_____ 15. A filamentous bacterium

_____ 16. Patient's own body is most common source

a. *Staphylococcus aureus*
b. *Legionella*
c. *Rhodococcus*
d. *Pseudomonas aeruginosa*
e. *Clostridium tetani*
f. *Clostridium perfringens*
g. *Actinomyces israelii*
h. *Pasteurella multocida*
i. *Rochalimea henselae*
j. *Spirillum minus*
k. *Sporotrix schenckii*

_____ 17. Causes rat bite fever

_____ 18. Soil is most common source

_____ 19. Results from animal bites

_____ 20. Organism grows in dead tissue

REVIEW QUESTIONS

1. Describe three reasons microorganisms in abscesses are not always killed even when antibiotics are used.

2. How does the presence of sutures affect the infecting dose of *Staphylococcus aureus* required to form an abscess?

3. What four factors are responsible for a shift in the spectrum of bacteria that cause surgical wound infections? Explain.

4. What two conditions contribute to the development of gas gangrene?

5. Why is *Pseudomonas* such a feared organism in burn wards?

6. Why is actinomycosis not a mycosis?

7. Complete the following table by listing the organisms usually associated with the type of wound.

TYPE OF WOUND	CAUSATIVE AGENT
Trauma wound	
Surgical wound	
Burn	
Animal bite	

27 BLOOD AND LYMPHATIC INFECTIONS: BACTERIAL

The blood and lymph systems are characteristically sterile. The introduction of infectious agents has serious consequences because the two systems can carry the organisms throughout the body and produce systemic infections. The blood and lymph have some natural resistance to infectious agents but when this resistance is overcome, serious disease results. Bacteremia is the simple presence of bacteria in the blood while septicemia usually implies the actual growth of bacteria in the blood stream. Infections range from chronic, such as subacute bacterial endocarditis, to acute as in the plaque.

KEY CONCEPTS

1. Infections of the heart and pericardium are dangerous because they can lead to impaired circulation of blood and damage to vital organs from a lack of oxygen.
2. Subacute bacterial endocarditis usually involves infection of a structurally abnormal heart by members of the normal skin or mouth flora.
3. The release of endotoxin in Gram-negative bacteremia tends to make it a more serious condition than Gram-positive bacteremia.

SUMMARY

I. Anatomy and Physiology
   A. The blood vascular system includes the heart, arteries, veins, and capillaries.
   B. The lymphatic system consists of the lymphatic vessels and lymph nodes. The blind-ended lymph vessels collect extracellular fluid and carry it back to the blood stream.

II. Bacterial Diseases of the Blood Vascular System
   A. Subacute bacterial endocarditis (SBE) involves the valves and lining of the heart chambers and is commonly caused by oral streptococci or *Staphylococcus epidermidis*. Infection usually begins in structurally abnormal heart chambers on valves previously damaged by disease, or on congenital abnormalities of the valves or chambers.
   B. Acute bacterial endocarditis is usually caused by virulent bacteria such as *Staphylococcus aureus* or *Streptococcus pneumoniae*.
   C. Septicemia usually results from bacteremia. It is often caused by Gram-negative organisms, mainly enterobacteria and anaerobes of the genus *Bacteroides*.

III. Bacterial Diseases Involving the Lymph Nodes and Spleen
   A. The mononuclear phagocyte system is involved in these diseases.
   B. Tularemia is often transmitted from wild animals to humans by insects and ticks. The cause is the Gram-negative aerobe, *Francisella tularensis*.
   C. Brucellosis is usually acquired from cattle or other domestic animals and is caused by species of *Brucella*. Pasteurization of milk is an important control measure.
   D. Plague, once pandemic, is now endemic in rodent populations. It is caused by *Yersinia pestis* and is transmitted to humans by fleas.

SELF-TEST OF READING MATERIAL

Use the list of diseases below to match their appropriate description.

a. subacute bacteria endocarditis
b. acute bacterial endocarditis
c. septicemia
d. tularemia
e. brucellosis
f. plague

_____ 1. *Streptococcus epidermidis* and alpha-hemolytic streps are causative agents.

_____ 2. It is endemic in rodent populations worldwide.

_____ 3. It is an occasional complication of infectious disease with bacteremia.

_____ 4. *Francisella tularensis* is the causative agent.

_____ 5. It causes a chronic infection of mammary glands and uterus in animals.

_____ 6. Enlarged lymph nodes called bubos are a hallmark.

_____ 7. Fleas serve as vectors.

_____ 8. The causative agents are the normal flora.

_____ 9. *S. aureus* and *Streptococcus pneumoniae* are the causative agents.

_____ 10. Shock is common.

_____ 11. Transmission by tick bites, inhalation, and skinning wild animals are possible.

_____ 12. Pneumonic form is transmitted by aerosols.

_____ 13. It commonly occurs in congenitally or disease damaged hearts.

_____ 14. *Yersinia pestis* is the causative agent.

_____ 15. The causative agents are usually of low virulence.

_____ 16. Another name is undulant fever.

_____ 17. Antibiotics that release endotoxins may make this infection worse.

_____ 18. This is a zoonosis.

_____ 19. This condition is most severe with Gram-negative bacteria.

_____ 20. Another name is Bang's disease.

_____ 21. The causative agents are usually high virulence.

_____ 22. This infection produces a steep-walled ulcer where it enters the skin.

_____ 23. This agent is commonly introduced into circulation by dental procedures.

_____ 24. Black Death is another name for this disease.

_____ 25. This is often seen as a complication of intravenous drug use.

REVIEW QUESTIONS

1. What types of antimicrobial agents are carried by the lymph?

2. Contrast acute and subacute bacterial endocarditis.

3. Describe the relationship between tumor necrosis factor and shock.

4. What is disseminated intravascular coagulation and how is it initiated?

5. Describe the changes to *Yersinia pestis* when it grows in a human host.

6. Compare and contrast bacteremia and septicemia.

7. What is the difference relative to transmission between bubonic and pneumonic plague?

8. A man in New Mexico contracted plague and died before it could be determined where he got the infection. According to his family, his only recent contact with any kind of animal occurred when he crawled under his house to remove a neighbor's puppy that had buried something and would not come out. How would you guess he got plague.

ANSWERS:
  Self-Test of Reading Material
   1. a 2. f 3. b 4. d 5. e 6. f 7. f 8. a 9. b 10. c 11. d 12. f 13. a 14. f 15. a 16. e 17. c 18. d,e
   19. c 20. e 21. b 22. d 23. a 24. f 25. b

28 BLOOD AND LYMPHATIC INFECTIONS: VIRAL AND PROTOZOAN

Viral and protozoan infections of the blood and lymph are serious diseases that affect many millions of people worldwide. Malaria still remains the greatest killer of mankind in spite of the successes of the 1950's in controlling the mosquito vector of this devastating disease. More than a million people a year still die from malaria. The difficulty with viral infections of the blood and lymph is the same as for any viral infection; the lack of effective means of treatment. This is no more painfully evident than in HIV infections that ultimately result in AIDS.

KEY CONCEPTS

1. In infectious mononucleosis, some of the patient's B lymphocytes become "immortal" because they are infected by the Epstein-Barr virus.
2. The symptoms of AIDS patients are caused mainly by the infections and tumors which complicate HIV disease.
3. Malaria is difficult to control because of treatment-resistant strains of the causative protozoan, and mosquito vectors resistant to insecticides.

SUMMARY

I. Viral Diseases of the Lymphoid System
   A. Infectious mononucleosis is a viral disease principally of B lymphocytes. The cause is the Epstein-Barr virus, which establishes a lifelong latent infection of lymphocytes, making them "immortal." The virus may be partly responsible for Burkitt's lymphoma and nasopharyngeal carcinoma.
   B. The acquired immune deficiency syndrome (AIDS) is a late manifestation of human immunodeficiency virus (HIV) infection. Relentless destruction of helper lymphocytes over months or years leads to AIDS.
   C. Yellow fever is caused by an arbovirus and is characterized by fever, jaundice, and hemorrhage.

II. Protozoan Infections
   A. Malaria is caused by four species of *Plasmodium* and is transmitted by the bite of the *Anopheles* mosquito.

TERMS AND DEFINITIONS

1. The stage of malaria that is injected into the human host by a mosquito is called a _____ .

2. A _____ is an organism in which a disease agent multiplies before transmission to a new host.

3. In an infection of malaria, infected erythrocytes break open and release _____ into the blood.

4. _____ , or a fuzzy white patch on the tongue, is a frequently encountered sign of AIDS that is probably caused by latent Epstein-Barr virus.

5. During malaria, some merozoites develop into _____ ,which are specialized sexual forms that complete development in the mosquito host.

6. _____ is a malignancy associated with AIDS that presents itself as purplish nodular skin swellings resembling bruises.

SELF-TEST OF READING MATERIAL

Use the list of diseases below to match their appropriate description.

    a.   infectious mononucleosis
    b.   acquired immunodeficiency syndrome
    c.   yellow fever
    d.   malaria

_____ 1. Name means "bad air."

_____ 2. This can be transmitted by exposure to semen or vaginal secretions, blood, or mother to baby.

_____ 3. The virus multiplies in the mosquito host.

_____ 4. Agent can be isolated from Burkitt's lymphoma.

_____ 5. Heterophile antibody is present in serum.

_____ 6. Infection has a high incidence in 15-24 year olds.

_____ 7. Recurrent bouts of fever are a sign of disease.

_____ 8. Saliva contains virus but is not significant in transmission.

_____ 9. Individuals with sickle cell anemia are resistant to infection.

_____ 10. Monkeys are reservoirs.

_____ 11. Infected B-lymphocytes can reproduce in culture indefinitely.

_____ 12. This infection has a mosquito vector.

_____ 13. During this infection, there is a gradual loss of T-4 helper cells over time.

_____ 14. This has been associated with malignancies in immunosuppressed patients.

_____ 15. Infection is caused by four species of *Plasmodium.*

_____ 16. Jaundice is a sign.

_____ 17. Pneumonia from *Pneumocystis carinii* is the cause of death in more than half of the cases.

_____ 18. Kissing disease is another name.

_____ 19. Disease causes more than a million deaths annually.

_____ 20. It is caused by the Epstein-Barr virus.

_____ 21. This disease may be related to the development of Burkitt's lymphoma.

_____ 22. T-4 helper cells are targets.

_____ 23. These infect erythrocytes.

_____ 24. This is a herpes virus.

_____ 25. This is a retrovirus.

REVIEW QUESTIONS

1. List and describe the diseases that frequently complicate AIDS.

2. Make a list of the behaviors that put people at risk for HIV infection.

3. What is a heterophile antibody?

4. Diagram the life cycle of *Plasmodium malariae*.

5. How does the T-4 count change during an HIV infection? When does it become AIDS?

ANSWERS:
Terms and Definitions
   1. sporozoite 2. biological vector 3. merozoites 4. hairy leukoplakia 5. gametocytes 6. Kaposi's sarcoma
Self-Test of Reading Material
   1. d 2. b 3. c 4. a 5. a 6. a 7. d 8. b 9. d 10. c 11. a 12. c,d 13. b 14. a 15. d 16. c 17. b 18. a
   19. d 20. a 21. a 22. b 23. d 24. a 25. b

29 *ANTIMICROBIAL AND ANTIVIRAL MEDICINES*

Treatment of infectious disease has obviously been a primary goal of medicine for centuries. Paul Ehrlich's search for the "magic bullet" that would kill an infectious agent without harming the patient was a systematic approach to the problem of antimicrobial therapy. The approach to the discovery of new antimicrobial agents today applies the knowledge of metabolism and genetics to solving the problem. Antimicrobial agents that interfere with processes unique to the pathogen will have the highest therapeutic index. While there are a considerable number of antimicrobial agents available, they fall into a few categories based either on their structure and/or their activity. This chapter summarizes the major groups of antimicrobial agents, their activity, and application.

KEY CONCEPTS

1. Certain chemicals selectively kill or inhibit the growth of one organism while sparing another.
2. Most antimicrobial medicines exploit the differences that are found between prokaryotic and eukaryotic cell structure and metabolism.
3. Laboratory tests of the susceptibility of microorganisms to antimicrobial medicines help predict the effectiveness of the medicines *in vivo*.
4. Mutations and transfer of genetic information have allowed microorganisms to develop resistance to each new antimicrobial medicine that has been developed.
5. Enzymes unique to viral replication provide potential sites of chemotherapeutic action.
6. Antiviral substances normally produced by the human body can now be produced *in vitro* and used in antiviral therapy.

SUMMARY

   I. Antimicrobial Chemotherapy Depends on the Principle of Selective Toxicity

  II. Antibiotics Are Antimicrobial Substances Produced Wholly or in Part by Certain Bacteria and Molds
       A. Chemical modification of antibiotics has produced families of antimicrobial medications having different properties.

 III. Antibacterial Medicines
       A. Synthetic medicines include sulfa drugs, trimethoprim, isoniazid, and others.
       B. Antibiotics include beta-lactams, tetracyclines, erythromycin, lincomycins, aminoglycosides, polypeptides, and rifamycins.

  IV. Modes of Action of Antimicrobial Medicines
       A. Competitive inhibition involves reversible impairment of an enzyme by a substance resembling the enzyme's normal substrate.
       B. Beta-lactams and certain other antibiotics act by impairing bacterial cell wall synthesis.
       C. Selective inhibition of microbial protein synthesis depends on differences between eukaryotic and prokaryotic ribosomes.
       D. A few antimicrobial agents are active against cytoplasmic membranes.
       E. Rifampin and the quinolones selectively inhibit bacterial nucleic acid synthesis.

   V. Bacterial Sensitivity Testing and Its Relationship to Antimicrobial Levels in Body Fluids
       A. Susceptibility to antibacterial medicines can be quantified by determining minimal inhibitory concentrations.
       B. The terms *sensitive* and *resistant* refer to whether a microorganism is likely to be treatable or not.

VI.   Limitations on the Value of Antibacterial Agents
    A.   A progressive increase in the percentage of resistant strains has occurred following the introduction of each new antimicrobial.
       1.   Selection of "wild" resistant variants.
       2.   Role of gene transfer in resistance.
       3.   Role of environment in resistance.
       4.   Mechanisms of resistance include enzymatic inactivation of the antimicrobial medication, decrease in permeability to the medication, and changes in the target substance so that it no longer binds the medication.
    B.   Toxins and host factors may also limit antimicrobial effectiveness.

VII.   Medicines that Act Against Eukaryotic Pathogens
    A.   Fungi.
       1.   Deep infections.
       2.   Superficial infections.
    B.   Protozoa.

VIII.   Medicines Active Against Viruses Include Amantadine, Acyclovir, Foscarnet, Purine and Pyrimidine Analogs, and Interferon
       1.   Amantadine prevents influenza A by interfering with viral uncoating.
       2.   Several base analogs inhibit reverse transcriptase.
       3.   Interferons interfere with translation of viral messenger RNA.

TERMS AND DEFINITIONS

1.   Antibiotics in which a portion is made by a microorganism and the remainder is made by a chemist

    are called _____ antibiotics.

2.   The lowest concentration of an antimicrobial agent capable of preventing growth is

    called the _____ concentration.

3.   The _____ is defined as the highest dose a patient can tolerate without toxic effects, divided by the dose required to control the microbial infection.

4.   Antibiotics are not directly involved in the growth of the organism that produces them and as such are known

    as _____ .

5.   _____ antibiotics show activity against at least some strains of both Gram-positive and Gram-negative species of bacteria.

6.   _____ colitis is an intestinal disease that is a potentially serious side effect of treatment with anitbiotics.

7.   _____ are enzymes that attack the ring structure of penicillin and its related antibiotics.

8. Plasmids that may contain genes for antimicrobial resistance to several antibiotics are

   called _____ factors or _____ plasmids.

9. _____ inhibitors bind to and irreversibly inactivate most ß-lactamases and are themselves inactivated in the process.

10. Chemical substances produced by some microorganisms that inhibit the growth of other microorganisms

    are called _____ .

SELF-TEST OF READING MATERIAL

Use the list of antimicrobial agents on the right to match with the appropriate description on the left.

_____ 1. Inactivates ß-lactamases

_____ 2. Used to treat bladder infections caused by *E. coli*

_____ 3. Can cause pseudomembranous colitis

_____ 4. Major use as an alternative to penicillin

_____ 5. Used against both bacteria and protozoa

_____ 6. Toxic but lowers blood cholesterol

_____ 7. Useful only for influenza A

_____ 8. Attaches to sterols in eukaryotic cell membranes

_____ 9. Used for topical treatment and made by *Bacillus*

_____ 10. Can cause aplastic anemia

_____ 11. Cannot be taken with milk because it is inactivated by ions such as calcium

_____ 12. Used in combination with sulfas to treat urinary tract infections

_____ 13. Active against bacterial cell wall

_____ 14. Used to treat tuberculosis

_____ 15. One of only a few antibiotics used to treat *Pseudomonas aeruginosa*

a. sulfa drugs
b. trimethoprim
c. quinolones
d. isoniazid
e. metronidazole
f. penicillins
g. cephalosporins
h. clavulanic acid
i. tetracyclines
j. chloramphenicol
k. neomycin
l. erythromycin
m. lincomycin
n. bacitracin
o. amphotericin B
p. amantadine

REVIEW QUESTIONS

1. What three groups of microorganisms produce antibiotics? Give an example of an organism from each group and an antibiotic it produces.

2. Outline the steps of the production of a new antibiotic.

3. What is clavulanic acid and what value is it in treating bacterial infections?

4. Give an example of an antifungal, an antiprotozoan, and an antiviral medicine. Why are infections by fungi and protozoa often more difficult to treat than bacterial infections?

5. What is the basis of selective toxicity and how does it relate to the theraputic index?

ANSWERS:
  Terms and Definitions
     1. semisynthetic 2. minimal inhibitory 3. theraputic ratio 4. secondary metabolites 5. broad-spectrum
     6. pseudomembranous 7. ß-lactamases 8. R/resistance 9. suicide 10. antibiotics
  Self-Test of Reading Material
     1. h 2. a 3. m 4. l 5. e 6. k 7. p 8. o 9. n 10. j 11. i 12. b 13. f,g 14. d 15. c

NOTES

30 MICROBIAL ECOLOGY AND TERRESTRIAL MICROBIOLOGY

We usually think of dirt as being a place of filth and infection; and it does contain a number of pathogenic organisms. However, the microbial populations of the soil are staggering both in number and in variety. The nature of the soil is dependent on its microbial populations. Microorganisms in the soil provide nutrients in their proper form to plants by processes ranging from nitrogen fixation to decomposition. A number of conditions of the microenvironment, in turn, influence the growth and well-being of the microbial population. Soil is a dynamic, living community. Microorganisms are even responsible for the sweet fresh smell of the soil that we so appreciate in the spring after a very hard, sterile winter.

KEY CONCEPTS

1. For the microorganism, the environment immediately surrounding it, its microenvironment, is most important.
2. Different microorganisms are capable of growing in a wide variety of environments but each will grow best in those environments for which it is well adapted.
3. The variety of microorganisms found in the soil is influenced by its physical nature and the available nutrients.
4. The microorganisms of the soil are essential in recycling the biologically important elements, oxygen, nitrogen, carbon, sulfur, and phosphorus.

SUMMARY

I. Principles of Microbial Ecology
    A. The major subunits of the biosphere are the ecosystems.
    B. Microenvironments are the most important considerations for bacterial cells.
    C. Microbial competition demands rapid reproduction and efficient use of nutrients.
    D. Microorganisms can both cause and adapt to environmental changes as in antibiotic resistance and souring of milk.
    E. Oligotrophs are organisms that can grow in very low nutrient environments.

II. Microorganisms and Soil
    A. Soil is a complex substance composed of both organic and inorganic materials.
    B. Soil teems with a variety of life forms including bacteria, algae, fungi, protozoa, nematodes, worms, and other eukaryotic organisms.

III. Environment Influences the Variety of Organisms that Are Present in Soil
    A. Moisture in the soil affects the oxygen supply.
        1. Waterlogged soils primarily support anaerobic organisms.
        2. Relatively few organisms grow in desert climates.
    B. Highly acid conditions inhibit the growth of most bacteria. Fungi generally are more tolerant of both high and low pH.
    C. Temperature regulates both the microbial metabolic activity rate as well as the type of organism that can grow.
        1. Most bacteria are mesophiles and grow between 20°C and 50°C.
        2. Psychrophiles grow below 20°C.
        3. Thermophiles grow above 50°C.
    D. The availability of organic matter tends to limit the size of the heterotrophic microbial population.

IV. Biochemical Cycling
    A. The organisms involved in recycling can be divided into three groups: the producers, the consumers and the decomposers.
    B. All ecosystems must have energy added to them, usually in the form of sunlight.

    C.   Oxygen cycles between respirers and photosynthesizers.

    D.   Carbon cycles between organic compounds and carbon dioxide.

        1.   Producers fix atmospheric CO_2 into organic compounds.

        2.   Decomposers use organic material as a source of carbon for various biological processes.

    E.   Nitrogen cycles between organic compounds and a variety of inorganic compounds.

        1.   Ammonification involves the degradation of cell components such as proteins to CO_2, ammonium and sulfate ions and water through a series of steps.

        2.   Nitrification is the microbial oxidation whereby ammonium is converted to nitrite and then to nitrate.

        3.   Denitrification occurs when some anaerobic bacteria use nitrate as a final electron acceptor, resulting in the liberation of N_2 and the loss of nitrogen to the ecosystem.

        4.   Nitrogen fixation involves prokaryotic microorganisms that are capable of reducing nitrogen gas to ammonium ion that is then used as the amino group of amino acids. Oxygen-sensitive enzymes called nitrogenases are responsible for nitrogen fixation. Some of these bacteria are free-living while others must establish a symbiotic relationship with plants.

    F.   Phosphorus also cycles between organic and inorganic compounds.

    G.   The sulfur cycle involves several important types of organisms.

  V.   Microbial Decomposition of Synthetic Chemicals

    A.   Most naturally occurring organic compounds are degraded by some microorganism.

    B.   Some synthetic compounds are not readily degraded.

        1.   DDT

        2.   2,4,5-T

        3.   PCBs

TERMS AND DEFINITIONS

1. Bacteria that grow best at temperatures between $20^\circ C$ and $50^\circ C$ are called _____ .

2. _____ is the chemical transformation of nitrogen from the atmosphere into a form that plants can use.

3. An _____ environment has a low nutrient content.

4. _____ is the conversion of an element from an inorganic form to an organic form.

5. Bacterial metabolites that give soil its characteristic odor are called _____ .

6. The environment immediately surrounding an individual cell is known as the _____ .

7. The community of living organisms in a given area that are interacting with the nonliving environment of that area form an _____ .

8. _____ are organisms that converts carbon dioxide into organic matter.

9. Organisms that metabolize organic matter synthesized by the _____ are called _____ .

10. The _____ digest and convert dead plant and animal material into small molecules that can be used by both the _____ and the _____ .

11. _____ is the loss of nitrogen from the soil when bacteria convert nitrate to gaseous nitrogen.

12. _____ is the conversion of an element from an organic form into an inorganic form.

13. The organic material in soil derived from the decomposition of plant, animal, and microbial matter

is called _____ .

14. _____ is the breakdown of protein that results in a very odorous product.

SELF-TEST OF READING MATERIAL

1. Phosphatase is
   - a. a mineral.
   - b. a carbonated fountain drink.
   - c. an enzyme that causes the mineralization of organic phosphate.
   - d. an enzyme that causes the mineralization of inorganic phosphate.
   - e. an enzyme that causes the immobilization of inorganic phosphate.

2. The largest group of bacteria in the soil are
   - a. actinomycetes.
   - b. *Clostridium.*
   - c. fungi.
   - d. *Bacillus.*
   - e. myxobacteria.

3. Nitrogen fixation is brought about by two types of microorganisms,
   - a. actinomycetes and fungi.
   - b. free-living and symbiotic.
   - c. *Bacillus* and *Clostridium.*
   - d. parasitic and symbiotic.
   - e. nitrifiers and denitrifiers.

4. The microorganisms associated with the sulfur cycle are
   - a. yellow-pigmented.
   - b. heterotrophs.
   - c. actinomycetes.
   - d. autotrophs.
   - e. aerobic.

5. Because bacteria are inhibited under highly acid conditions, acid soils will be dominated by
   - a. fungi.
   - b. protozoa.
   - c. nitrogen fixers.
   - d. actinomycetes.
   - e. Acid soil does not have any significant microbial populations.

REVIEW QUESTIONS

1. Describe the succession of organism in a carton of milk that has not been refrigerated. Is this all bad? Explain.

2. Why are herbicides and pesticides so harmful to the ecology of the soil?

3. What conditions affect the growth of microorganisms in the soil?

4. Outline the steps of one of the geochemical cycles.

5. What is the microenvironment of a cell? Why is it important?

NOTES

NOTES

31 MICROBIOLOGY AND ECOLOGY OF AQUATIC ENVIRONMENTS

Nearly all water contains microorganisms of some type. Aquatic environments range from extremely hypertonic (salty) such as the Great Salt Lake to nearly pure distilled water stored in plastic carboys. Microorganisms live in the entire range of aquatic environments. Most environments have their own natural populations of organisms as well as many that are contaminated from outside sources such as sewage. This chapter looks at the nature of aquatic environments and the organisms that inhabit them as well as the effects of pollution on aquatic environments.

KEY CONCEPTS

1. Because water is an excellent solvent, many otherwise useful substances can adversely affect its quality.
2. Factors such as temperature, pH, and dissolved minerals determine which microorganisms can live in water.
3. The available nutrients in water determine the variety of microorganisms that can live in it.

SUMMARY

I. The Nature of Aquatic Environments
  A. Water is an extremely efficient solvent and most water is a dilute solution of any number of substances.
  B. Rain water usually has few impurities.
    1. Acid rain occurs because of air pollution.
    2. Lakes and streams can be seriously affected by acid rain.
  C. The properties of water depend on where the water comes from or what it passes through.
  D. Freshwater environments are diverse.
    1. Eutrophication of freshwater occurs when nutrients are added to the water.
    2. These nutrients can come from human activities.
  E. Marine environments differ depending on their proximity to land.
    1. Open oceans are nutrient poor.
    2. Estuaries are rich in nutrients.

II. The Microbial Flora of Aquatic Environments
  A. The microbial population of freshwater is dictated by the available nutrients.
  B. Seawater contains different microbial species than freshwater.
    1. Hydrostatic pressure determines which organisms can survive.
    2. It is difficult to measure organisms in seawater because they are so sparse.

III. The Consequences of Water Pollution
  A. Pollution with pathogenic organisms can cause disease epidemics.
  B. Eutrophication of freshwater by human pollution is an important problem that can be reversed.

IV. Microorganisms and Pollution

TERMS AND DEFINITIONS

1. The nutrient enrichment of natural waters is called _____ .

2. Bacteria with stalks that use them to survive in conditions of low nutrient availability are

   called _____ bacteria.

3. _____ are microorganisms that can survive great pressures such as at the depths of the oceans.

4. The accumulation of degraded plant material compressed by the weight of the water over it in swamps and bogs

   is known as _____ .

5. The_____ zone is the upper layer of a water column where light can penetrate.

6. Aquatic systems low in nutrients are said to be _____ .

7. _____ are material that wash from a particular area and are carried into the water.

8. The _____ column is a device used to isolate bacteria from the sediment from a lake or stream.

9. The transition zone where freshwater and seawater mix is known as an _____ .

10. _____ is an enzyme associated with the cell wall of some aquatic bacteria that break down plants and algae in an aquatic environment.

SELF-TEST OF READING MATERIAL

1. When a lake undergoes stratification
   a. warmer layers on the top become anaerobic.
   b. colder layers on the bottom become oxygenated.
   c. warmer layers on the top become oxygenated.
   d. colder layers on the bottom become anaerobic.
   e. Two of the above are correct.

2. *Mycobacterium marinum* cause a tuberculosis-like disease in fish.
   a. True
   b. False

3. A large proportion of the oxygen in our atmosphere is produced by
   a. marine algae.
   b. dinoflagellates.
   c. ocean vents.
   d. photosynthetic bacteria.
   e. zooplankton.

4. The salt content of seawater averages
   a. 0%
   b. 30%
   c. 1.0%
   d. 3.5%
   e. 0.9%

5. The sulfur and nitrogen oxides in the atmosphere come primarily from
   a. geothermal recycling.
   b. agricultural fertilization.
   c. burning fossil fuels.
   d. marine environments.
   e. volcanoes.

REVIEW QUESTIONS

1. Describe the Canadian experiment. What were the significant conclusions about acid rain?

2. Is eutrophication a natural or artificial process? What is accelerated eutrophication? What can be done about it?

3. Compare marine and freshwater environments.

4. Describe three activities of microorganisms in aquatic environments.

5. Describe stratification in lakes.

32 MICROBIOLOGY OF WASTE TREATMENT

The treatment of our household and industrial waste is a problem that literally grows larger each day. The not too dissimilar threat of cholera was the driving force behind the development of sewage systems in the last century. Today our environment and, possibly again, our health is being threatened by the wastes that we are producing. We are developing new solutions to help solve these problems but they at first appear expensive until we seriously consider the cost if we do nothing. The good news is that individuals can do something to help. Composting by individuals will remove some 20-30% of the burden of solid waste disposal.

KEY CONCEPTS

1. Proper sewage treatment is necessary to ensure the health of the community.
2. Proper sewage treatment depends on the stabilization of wastes by microorganisms.
3. Pathogenic bacteria are usually eliminated by the secondary sewage treatment process.
4. Innovations such as trickling filters and artificial wetlands are good solutions to small scale sewage treatment problems.
5. Both backyard and commercial composting reduce the need for large landfills for disposal of solid waste.

SUMMARY

I. The Microbiology of Waste Treatment
    A. Sewage contains a variety of substances.
        1. Human wastes.
        2. Industrial wastes.
        3. Food wastes.
    B. Microorganisms degrade the components of sewage to inorganic compounds.
    C. Microorganisms reduce the biological oxygen demand (BOD) of sewage.
        1. Primary treatment.
        2. Secondary treatment.
        3. Tertiary treatment.
    D. Sewage can also be treated on a small scale using lagooning, trickling filters, septic tanks, and artificial wetlands.
    E. Using treated waste residues is still a problem.

II. Microbiology of Solid Waste Treatment
    A. Sanitary landfills have been a low-cost method for disposing of solid waste.
    B. Recycling programs and other means are being used to reduce the amount of garbage going into landfills.
    C. Backyard and commercial composting both help reduce the amount of material in landfills and help add nutrients to the soil.

TERMS AND DEFINITIONS

1. The mechanism by which populations of aerobic organisms stabilize sewage at most secondary treatment plants

   is called _____ method.

2. _____ is the conversion by microorganisms of organic materials to inorganic

   forms. Another term for this process is _____ .

3. A method of sewage treatment that can be used by small communities and involves a series of ponds designed for

   aerobic and anaerobic stabilization is known as _____ .

4. _____ spray controlled amounts of sewage over beds of coarse gravel and rocks where communities of organisms degrade the sewage.

5. _____ treatment involves the chemical and biological processes of converting remaining organic materials in sewage into odorless, inorganic substances that can be reused.

6. Within a sewage _____, anaerobic organisms act on the solids through anaerobic stabilization.

7. The term _____ designates the oxygen-consuming property of a waste-water sample and is roughly proportional to the amount of degradable organic material present.

8. A _____ tank relies on anaerobic digestion and the proper distribution of the overflow into a drainage field.

9. In _____, sewage is channeled into shallow ponds where it remains for several days to a month.

10. The method of solid waste disposal where the waste is covered over each day with dirt is a _____ .

SELF-TEST OF READING MATERIAL

1. Which of the following was primarily responsible for the development of sewer systems?
   a. no more sites for landfills
   b. cholera
   c. plague
   d. community betterment groups
   e. odors

2. Every day each American produces an average of _____ gallons of sewage.
   a. 1.2
   b. 12
   c. 120
   d. 1200
   e. 5

3. Which of the following treatments removes phosphates and nitrates from sewage?
   a. primary
   b. artificial wetlands
   c. secondary
   d. digester
   e. tertiary

4. What type of gas produced in a home digester can be used to heat homes and cook food?
   a. oxygen
   b. methane
   c. propane
   d. hydrogen
   e. carbon dioxide

5. During which of the following treatments are pathogens generally eliminated?
   a. primary
   b. artificial wetlands
   c. secondary
   d. digester
   e. tertiary

6. The biochemical oxygen demand roughly measures the amount of _____ in water.
   a. degradable organic material
   b. oxygen
   c. degradable inorganic material
   d. All of the above.
   e. Only a and c are correct.

REVIEW QUESTIONS

1. Describe the levels of sewage treatment. Do you know what level your community uses?

2. What is the BOD and how is it measured?

3. Contrast the activated sludge method and a digester.

4. How effective is each of the stages of sewage treatment in removing bacterial pathogens? Viral pathogens?

5. What are the disadvantages of a sanitary landfill?

6. How can composting help?

7. List the steps for making a compost pile at home.

ANSWERS:
Terms and Definitions
  1. activated sludge 2. stabilization/mineralization 3. artificial wetlands 4. trickling filters 5. secondary 6. digester
  7. biochemical oxygen demand 8. septic 9. lagooning 10. sanitary landfill
Self-Test of Reading Material
  1. b 2. c 3. e 4. b 5. c 6. a

33 THE MICROBIOLOGY OF FOOD AND BEVERAGES

There is both good news and bad news concerning the activities of microorganisms in food and beverages. The bad news is that microorganisms are responsible for the spoilage of food. When this spoilage prevents food from being used in a world of many starving people, the loss is tragic. We usually, however, measure the loss in terms of dollars and it can be extensive. The good news is that microorganisms are also responsible for many of our fine and delicious foods. In some respects this food production is actually controlled spoilage. Many of our fermented foods were produced initially because the fermentation also preserves them. Knowing what spoils food can teach us how to preserve it.

KEY CONCEPTS

1. A variety of microorganisms can use human food as a growth medium, degrade it, and spoil it for human consumption.
2. Food spoilage can be eliminated or retarded by altering the conditions under which microorganisms grow.
3. Heating, drying, refrigerating, freezing, irradiating and adding chemicals are some of the ways to control the growth of microorganisms on food.
4. A variety of foods such as bread, cheese, and alcoholic beverages result from metabolic activities of microorganisms.

SUMMARY

I. Microorganisms Are Responsible for Food Spoilage
   A. Food spoilage microorganisms are usually nonpathogenic for humans.
   B. *Pseudomonas* species are the most common food spoilage organisms.
   C. Food poisoning is often caused by *Staphylococcus aureus*.

II. Spoilage Organisms Require Specific Conditions to Grow
   A. Water activity.
   B. pH.
   C. Availability of nutrients.

III. Protection of Food by Naturally Occurring Antimicrobial Substances

IV. Food Preservation
   A. Food contaminants can be killed by high-temperature treatment.
      1. The primary concern is the destruction of *Clostridium botulinum* spores.
      2. The higher the temperature, the less time is needed.
      3. The more microorganisms present the longer the time and the higher the temperature required.
      4. The condition of the microorganism and the type of environment is important to know.
   B. Pasteurization kills many potentially pathogenic organisms but does not sterilize the food.
   C. Growth of spoilage organisms is slowed or halted by low-temperature treatment.
      1. Low temperatures, such as a refrigerator, slow the growth of organisms, but do not kill them.
      2. Freezing stops the growth of microorganisms but may not kill them.
   D. Desiccation, or drying, prevents microbial growth by reducing the water activity.
      1. Drying stops the growth of bacteria but does not kill all bacteria.
      2. Sugaring, salting, and smoking also act to reduce the amount of water in foods.
      3. Lyophilization is freeze-drying.
   E. Chemicals are added to food for preservation.
   F. Irradiation can be used for some food preservation but thus far has limited use.
      1. Microwaves.
      2. Gamma irradiation.

V.   Control of Microbial Hazards in Food
   A.   The United States has strict standard of control.
   B.   Food-borne illnesses occur in spite of these strict controls.
      1.   Food-borne infections.
      2.   Food-borne intoxications.
   C.   Some diseases are transmitted through food.

VI.   Microbes Are Used in the Production of Food and Beverages.
   A.   Milk products are made using lactic acid bacteria.
      1.   Yogurt
      2.   Cheese
   B.   Pickles and sauerkraut are also made using lactic acid bacteria.
   C.   Soy sauce is traditionally made by fermenting soy beans.
   D.   Bread is produced with the yeast *Saccharomyces cerevesiae*.
   E.   Alcoholic beverages are produced by fermentation usually with *Saccharomyces*.
      1.   Wine—grapes and other fruits are fermented to produce wines.
      2.   Beer is made by fermenting starch.
      3.   Distilled spirits.
      4.   Vinegar is made by *Acetobacter* and *Gluconobacter* species oxidizing alcohol to acetic acid.

TERMS AND DEFINITIONS

1.   During the production of soy sauce, the initial mixture of salt soybeans, wheat, and the mold, *Aspergillus oryzae*,

   is called _____ .

2.   The _____ is a measure of the amount of moisture available in foods.

3.   The enzyme added to milk during the production of cheese to cause it to coagulate is called _____ .

4.   To preserve vegetables, they are pickled in _____ .

5.   The dried flowers of a vine-like plant that are added to beer and produce the typical bitter taste are

   called _____ .

6.   _____ is another term for freeze drying.

7.   During beer making, the conversion of the barley starch to sugars is called _____ .

8.   In the making of cheeses, following the treatment of the milk with an enzyme, the coagulated protein called

   the _____ is separated from the liquid portion, called the _____ .

9.   After beer has been malted, the germinated grain is added to warm water to give an extract called _____ .

10.   The starch digesting enzyme is called _____ .

SELF-TEST OF READING MATERIAL

1. Which of the following is essential for the growth of all microorganisms in food and beverages?
   a. vitamins
   b. oxygen
   c. water
   d. sugars
   e. darkness

2. Bacteria with an optimum growth temperature around 10°C are capable of causing spoilage in a refrigerator and are called
   a. thermophiles
   b. mesophiles
   c. acidophiles
   d. psychopathic
   e. psychrophiles

3. Which group of bacteria is most likely to spoil a freshwater trout caught in a cold mountain stream and preserved in salt?
   a. psychrophiles
   b. halophiles
   c. anaerobes
   d. thermophiles
   e. rockfordphiles

4. Salts and sugars preserve foods because they
   a. make them acid.
   b. produce a hypotonic environment.
   c. deplete nutrients.
   d. produce a hypertonic environment.
   e. provide nutrients.

5. Acidic foods are more likely to be spoiled by
   a. bacteria.
   b. fungi.
   c. acid sensitive organisms.
   d. thermophiles.
   e. Acid foods are rarely spoiled.

6. Sulfur dioxide is added to wine during its production to enhance the growth of *Lactobacillus*.
   a. True
   b. False

7. The thermal death time for determining sterilizing conditions, takes into consideration
   a. the temperature.
   b. the time.
   c. standard conditions of killing.
   d. the organism.
   e. All of the above are taken into consideration.

8. For proper pasteurization, ice cream would have to be pasteurized longer and at higher temperatures than milk.
   a. True
   b. False

9. The colors and flavors of red wine come from
   a. the grape skins and seeds.
   b. distillation.
   c. natural additives.
   d. the yeasts used.
   e. natural and artificial additives.

10. Vinegar production requires
    a. aerobic conditions.
    b. ethyl alcohol.
    c. anaerobic conditions.
    d. a and b are correct.
    e. b and c are correct.

REVIEW QUESTIONS

1. List the factors that influence the growth of microorganisms in foods and beverages. How are these factors any different from those that influence microbial growth in general?

2. Describe the three methods of pasteurization.

3. List the four categories of food-borne illnesses and give examples.

4. If your jar of pickles spoiled, would you expect to isolate fungi or bacteria? Why?

5. What factors impact on the proper times and temperatures that foods must be subjected to in order to kill the microorganisms present?

6. When foods are salted, smoked, or sugared, what actually prevents the growth of unwanted microorganisms in each case?